ROGER BIRCH

LAYOUT, DESIGN & ILLUSTRATION BY IAN MCALISTER

First Published in Britain in 2006

Front cover photographs by Roger Birch
Dinosaurs by kind permission of J. Sibbick

British Library Cataloguing-in Publication Data
A CIP record for this title is available from the British Library

ISBN 0-9551259-0-1

ISBN 978-09551259-0-4

Published by Roger Birch 2006
rdb@collyers.ac.uk

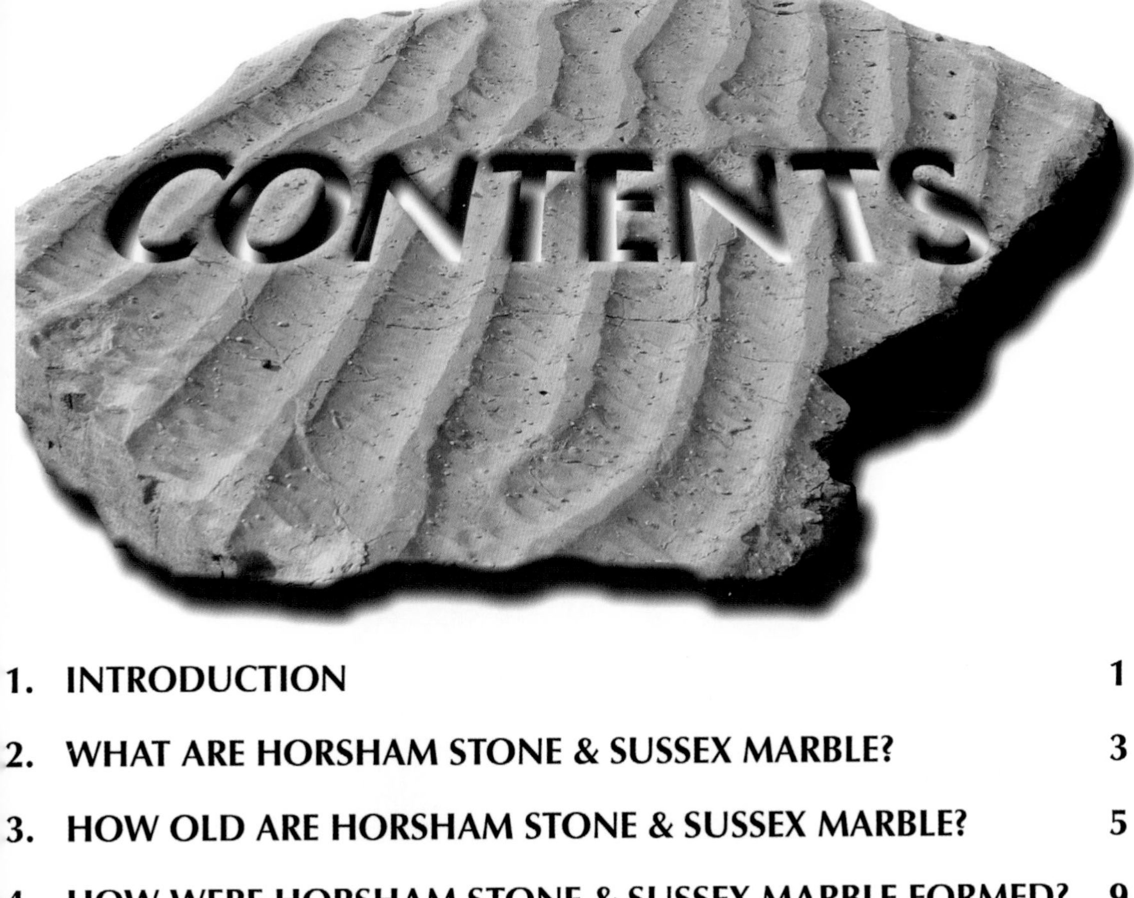
CONTENTS

About the Author

Roger Birch has lived in Sussex for 30 years and has taught a wide range of adult education and degree courses in Surrey and Sussex. He teaches geology and environmental science at Collyers College, Horsham and is currently an associate lecturer at Sussex University.

Dedication

To my parents who introduced me to the rocks and the fascinating landscape of the Peak District. As a young student I spent many weekends walking the limestone dales and wild moors of the Pennines.

To Angela and Jo who have encouraged me to stick at writing the book and for putting up with living in a house full of rocks and fossils!

1 INTRODUCTION

This book aims to describe the geological background of two famous local building stones, Horsham Stone and Sussex Marble and to trace the use of these rocks as building and ornamental stones for nearly 2,000 years. West Sussex has a rich historical and religious heritage found in castles, churches, medieval houses and decorative stonework.

This book has been designed to be an informative and visual introduction to the great wealth and variety of Horsham Stone and Sussex Marble. West Sussex is not a county where dozens of quarries dot the landscape or where dry stone walls weave their way across the countryside. The geology of West Sussex has created a landscape of clay vales, sandstone heaths and ridges and chalk downland. The landscape is low-lying compared with many other areas of Britain.

The geological story explained in this book is one of intricate detail and patient detective work. Hidden within hundreds of metres of Wealden Clay and sandstone is a truly remarkable story that started over 130 million years ago in the Cretaceous period. Our story begins with the introduction to Horsham Stone and Sussex Marble and the ancient geological environment in which the rocks were deposited as sediments in the tropical Wealden delta, millions of years ago. A look inside Horsham Stone and Sussex Marble reveals the remarkable detail of fossils and structures trapped in a geological time capsule.

The history of the use of these rocks concludes our story, a story that goes back to Roman times. The historical development of the county is reflected in the use of the building stones. Horsham Stone and Sussex Marble possessed intrinsic properties of strength, longevity, aesthetic appearance and economic value.

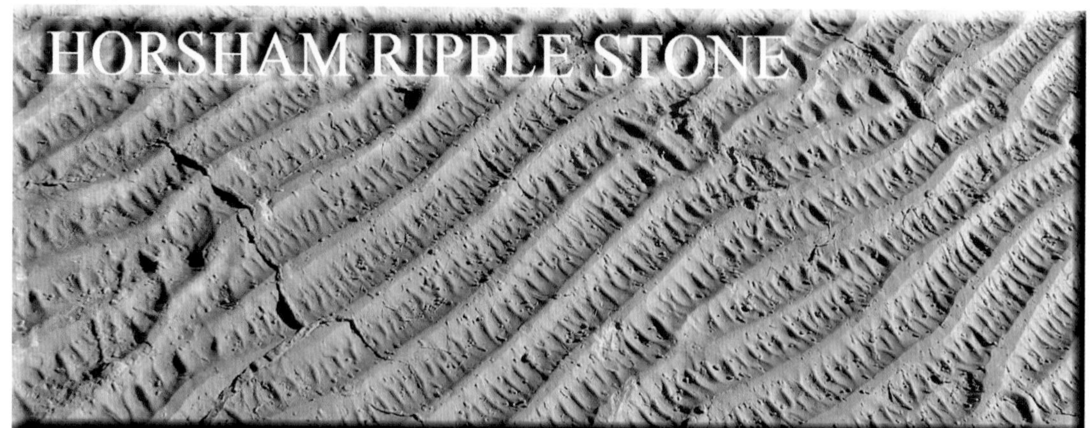

Geological terminology has been kept to a minimum but there is sufficient detail to enable readers to feel that they have entered the world of geology in a painless way! A full glossary is provided at the end of the book. The latest ideas and research have been blended into the story and a number of photographs of fossils have been kindly provided by amateur geologists who spend many weekends searching for new and exciting finds.

After reading this book I hope that readers will feel confident to travel around the region and start to interpret the geological story beneath the landscape. A list of places to visit is included so that many examples used in the book can be studied first-hand.

I hope that the book brings alive the geological history that exists in the rocks. It is a story of tropical landscapes uniquely preserved by the Earth's processes and continues to more recent times with humans digging the rocks from the ground, carving and shaping them into objects of beauty.

Roger Birch
Horsham, December 2005.

2 WHAT ARE HORSHAM STONE & SUSSEX MARBLE?

A geologist would describe Horsham Stone as a calcareous, flaggy sandstone. The rock extends for several kilometres running around Horsham in an arc-like pattern, where it occurs as a number of seams that can be found just below the soil. Horsham Stone is famous for its ripple-marked appearance and paving slabs still showing these ripples, despite hundreds of years of weathering and the trampling of feet, can be found in many churchyards.

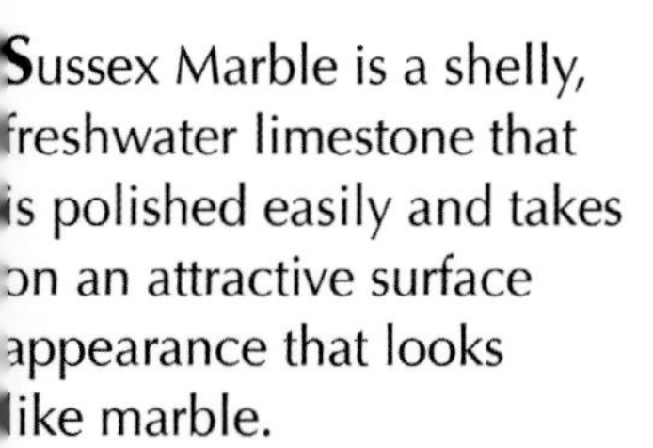

Sussex Marble is a shelly, freshwater limestone that is polished easily and takes on an attractive surface appearance that looks like marble.

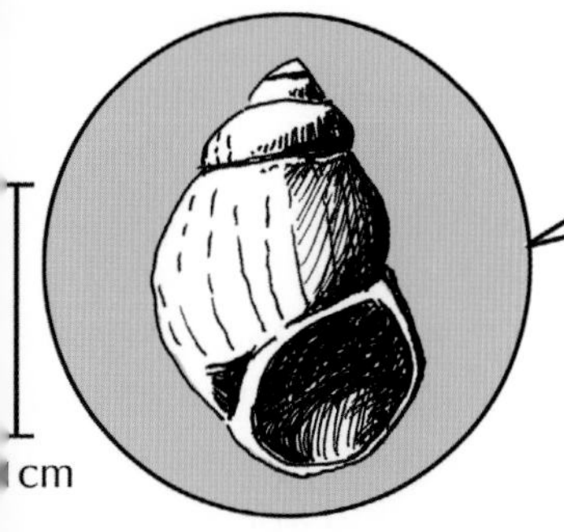

Gastropod shell, Viviparus

Carving on a Sussex Marble fireplace in Horsham Museum, dated 17th century

Sussex Marble has been given many names over the centuries. The names refer to the locality from which it was quarried eg Laughton Marble, Petworth Marble, Charlwood Marble and Bethersden Marble. Historical texts use the term 'winklestone '.

In the nineteenth century, geological maps and surveys used the palaeontological identification name of 'Paludina' Limestone. 'Paludina' is an old name for the key fossil found in the rock, which is a freshwater gastropod or snail shell. This name is used still on current geological maps and in scientific papers.

Horsham Stone and Sussex Marble are types of sedimentary rocks. All rocks on Earth are classified into three major groups. The first group is igneous rock that was once molten magma. We can see these rocks forming today in Iceland and Hawaii. The second group is metamorphic rock which forms deep in the Earth's crust where tremendous forces of heat and pressure transform rocks into new rock types. The last group is sedimentary rock. This makes up the most common rock group on Earth. These rocks are made up of the weathered remains of other rocks that have been reduced to pebbles, sand and silt over millions of years of erosion.

Ripples forming on West Wittering beach.

Horsham Stone is a type of sandstone composed of millions of tiny sand grains. The photographs on this page show sand being swept along by gentle waves, forming ripple-marks on West Wittering beach, near Chichester. By studying how sediments are transported and deposited today, geologists can visualise how sedimentary rocks formed millions of years ago. Horsham Stone, with its famous ripple marks, probably formed in a similar way to the ripples on the sandbanks and beaches around West Wittering today.

Horsham Stone

Sussex Marble is a type of sedimentary rock called limestone. It is composed of thousands of small snail shells, or gastropods These shells are fossils squeezed and compressed together and then cemented into hard rock by a mineral called calcite.The photographs below show some of the different coloured types of Sussex Marble. Whole fossils and fragments of crushed and broken fossils are clear to see. The different colours are due to varying amounts of white calcite, mud, silt and iron impurity. A photograph of hundreds of shells swept up by waves onto a beach in Sussex shows us how water currents and wave action can sort and collect shells of a similar species and size. The Sussex Marble gastropods were probably swept up onto sandbanks or coastlines in a large delta or estuary over 130 million years ago.

2cm

Brown

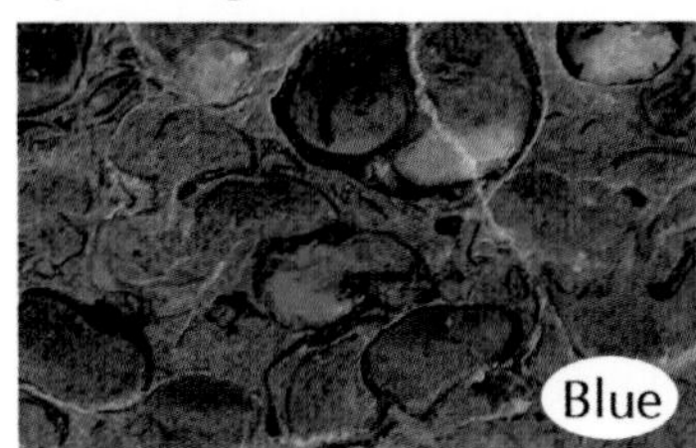
Blue

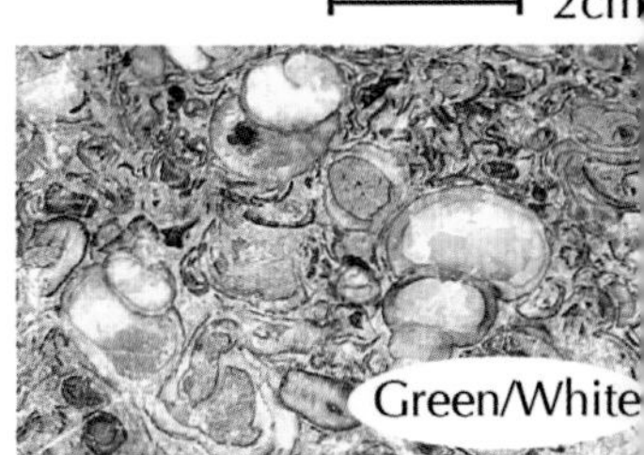
Green/White

3 HOW OLD ARE HORSHAM STONE & SUSSEX MARBLE?

The rocks found around Horsham belong to the Cretaceous period. Geological time is recorded in millions of years and geologists estimate that the Earth is over 4,600 million years old. The story for West Sussex begins around 130 million years ago when life on the planet had evolved into a wide range of complex ecosystems – this was the age of the dinosaurs. The fossils found in quarries around the county give geologists important clues as to the environmental conditions which existed millions of years ago. The reconstruction of these ancient conditions enables the palaeoenvironment to be visualised. Films like 'Jurassic Park' and the television programme, 'Walking with Dinosaurs' have done much to give us an insight into life in the geological past.

Geological time is divided up into major chapters which form the Geological Column, each chapter or period having a particular name. The Cretaceous period is the chapter in the Earth's history that covers the geological story for the rocks in Sussex. The period runs from 130 million years ago to 65 million years ago. After meticulous investigation over the past 250 years, geologists have sub-divided the Cretaceous period into rock units such as the Chalk, Upper Greensand, Gault Clay, Lower Greensand, Weald Clay and the Hastings Beds. The geographical region of the Weald runs through the centre of East and West Sussex on an east to west axis. The core of the Weald reveals some of the oldest rocks of the Cretaceous period, the Hastings Beds. These rocks create the unique higher landscape known as the High Weald, a landscape of densely wooded hills cut by narrow, steep river valleys.

Geological Time Chart

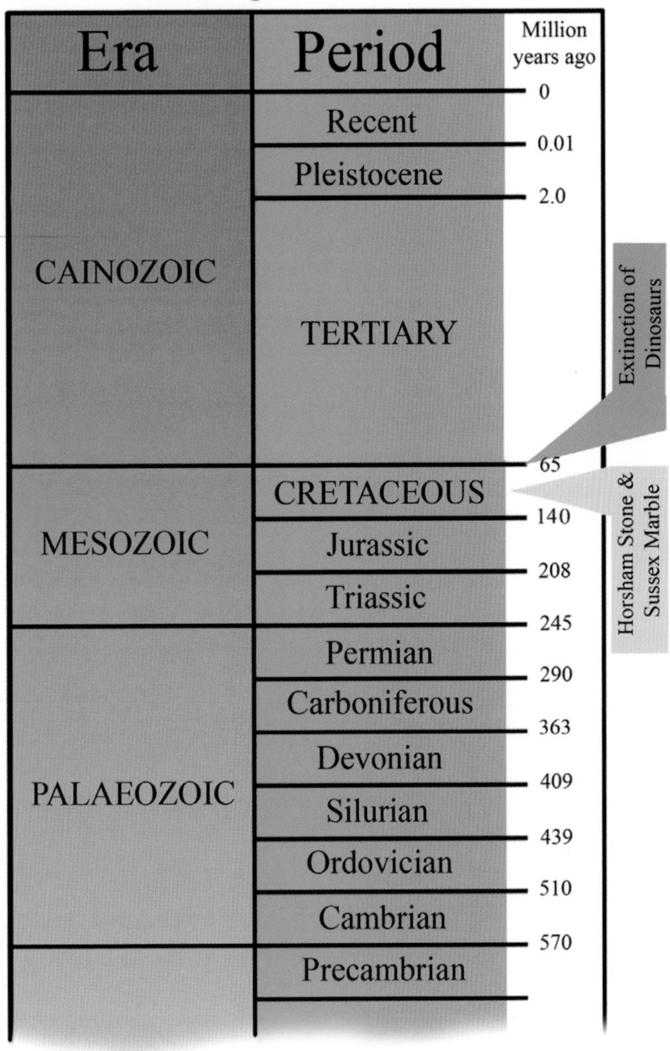

There are two types of 'Paludina' Limestone; the Large 'Paludina' and the Small 'Paludina'.

The Large refers to the fact that the shells are a slightly bigger species than those found in th smaller 'Paludina' Limestone. The Large 'Paludina' shells are usually 15-20mm in length and the Small 'Paludina' 10mm. The Large 'Paludina' Limestone is younger geologically than the Small 'Paludina', which occurs in thinner seams and was not used as much for ornamental purposes. Both these types of limestone can be traced across large areas of the Weald. The main outcrops for both beds run from Charlwood in the north, west towards Plaistow and Rudgwick and then south to Billingshurst. The beds then continue eastwards into East Sussex towards Lewes and run into Kent as far as Ashford.

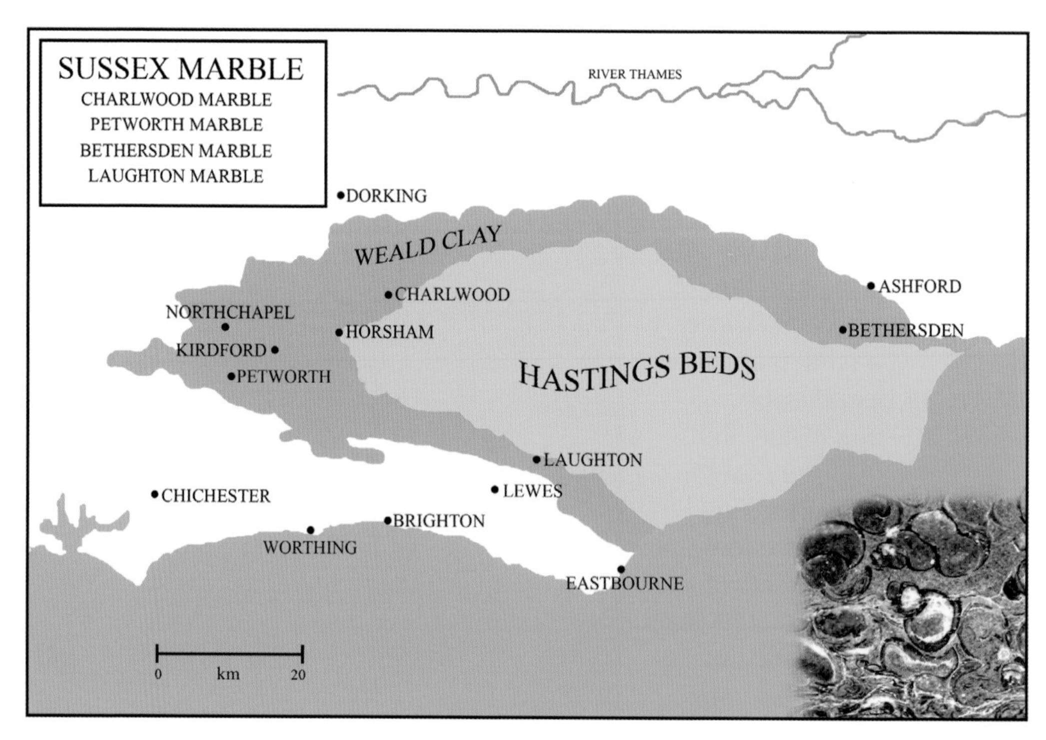

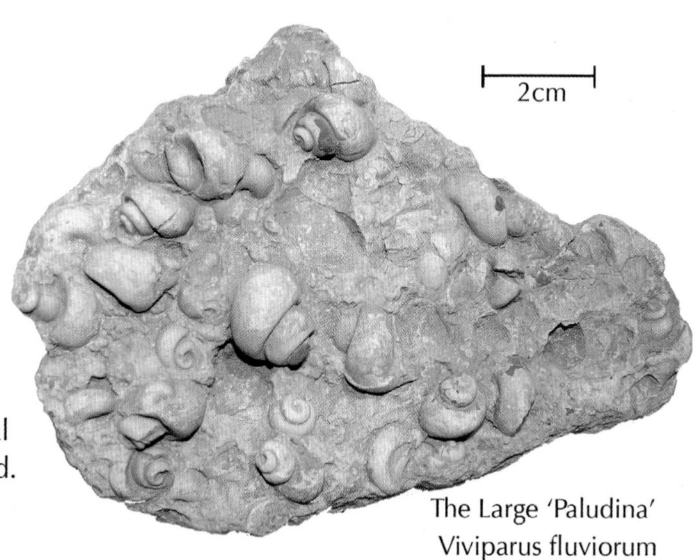

Detailed analysis of the freshwater gastropod has resulted in the fossil being re-named Viviparus.
The Large 'Paludina' is now called Viviparus fluviorum and the Small 'Paludina' is called Viviparus infracretacicus.
Throughout this book the traditional name of Sussex Marble will be used.

The Large 'Paludina'
Viviparus fluviorum

Geological Map of East and West Sussex

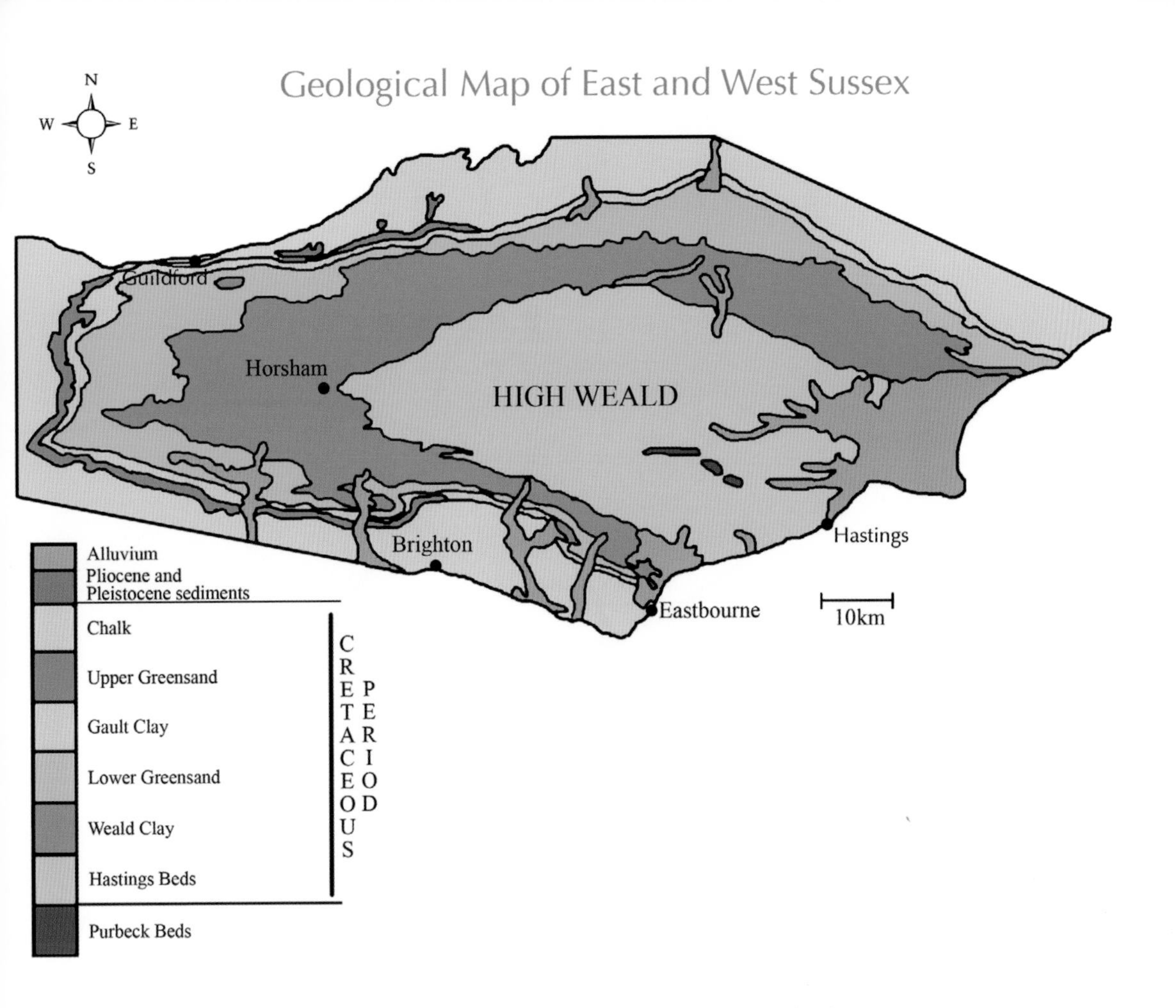

Geological Sketch Section showing rock formation across the Weald Anticline

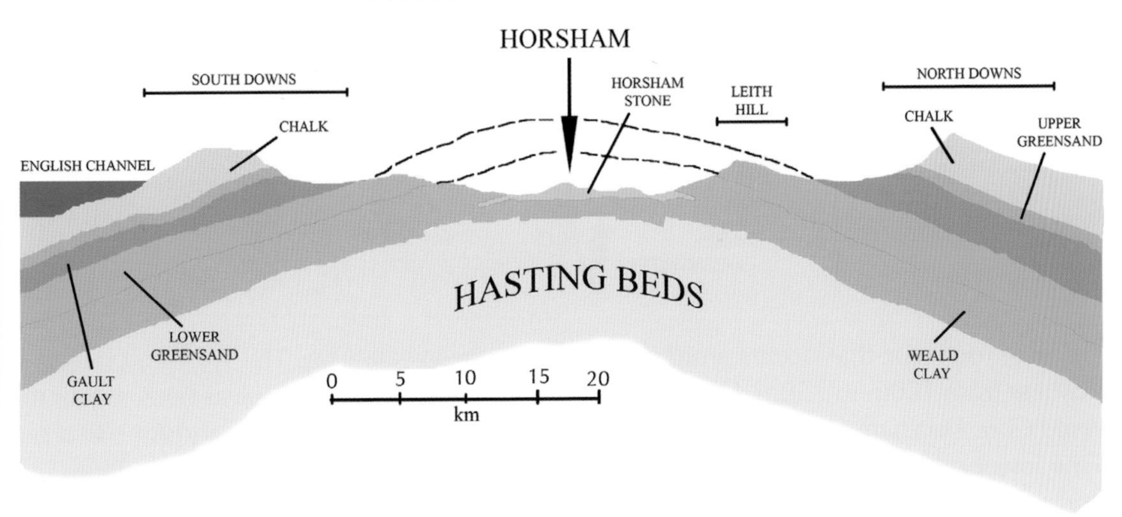

The rocks of Sussex have been buckled and folded into a massive dome-shaped fold called the Weald Anticline.

Map showing the outcrop of Horsham Stone and the location of old quarries

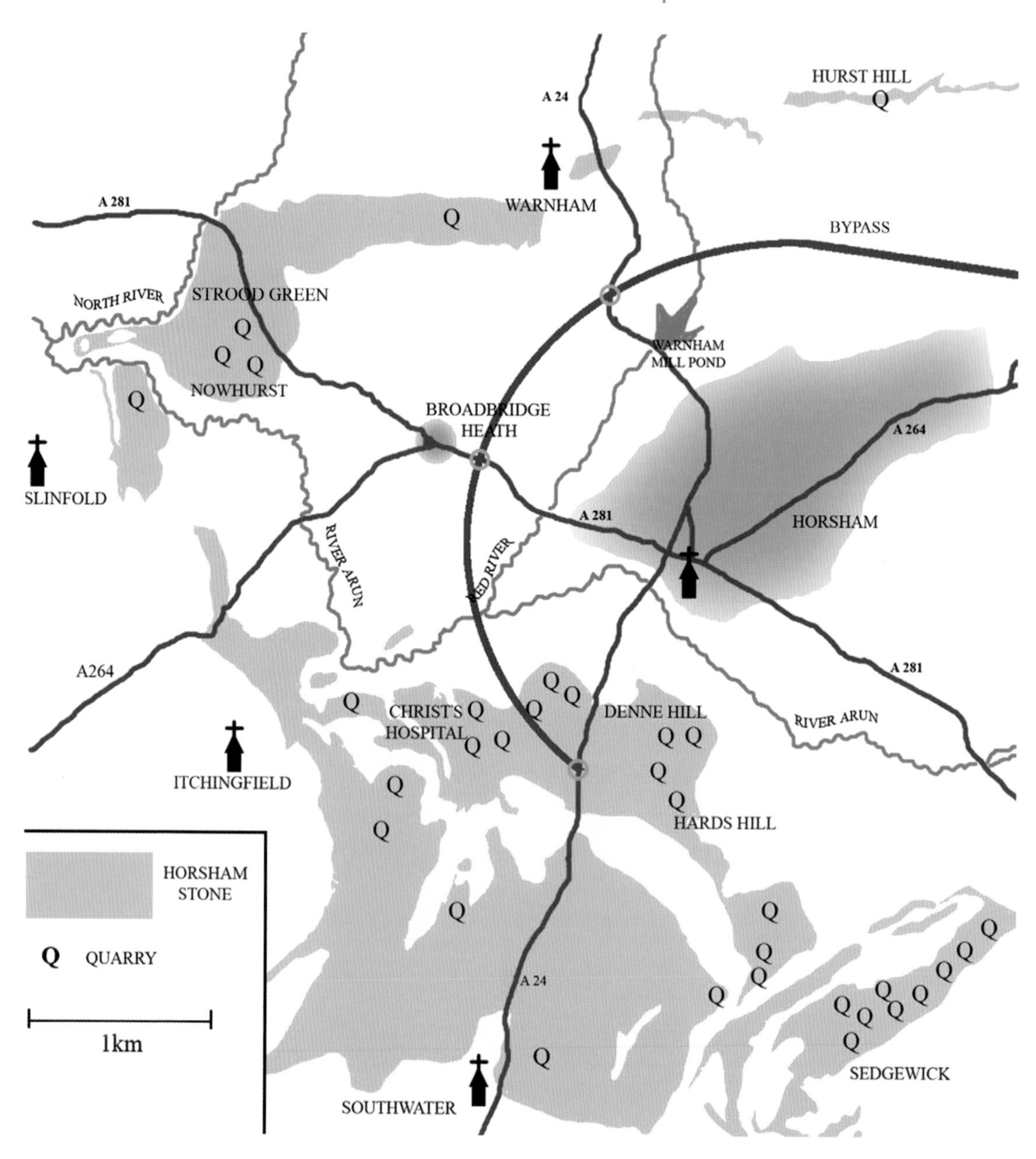

The main rock type that occurs around Horsham is the Weald Clay. This rock unit ranges in thickness from 100m to 750m. Horsham Stone and Sussex Marble occur as beds within the Weald Clay. Horsham Stone refers to a number of hard, resistant beds of sandstone that occur in the lower part of the Weald Clay succession and create low scarps and gentle slopes. A good example of this is the steep ridge that occurs just south of Horsham, at Denne Hill. This ridge runs eastwards towards Nuthurst, Sedgewick Park and Maplehurst. Historical records show that numerous shallow pits were dug all along this ridge in the seventeenth and eighteenth centuries. These shallow pits are still visible as slight depressions, despite being covered with undergrowth and trees.

4 HOW WERE HORSHAM STONE & SUSSEX MARBLE FORMED?

The story begins over 130 million years ago in the Lower Cretaceous period when Britain was quite different from the familiar shape it is today and had a different climate. It is estimated that the latitude for Britain was approximately 30 degrees north of the equator. For comparison, that is the latitude of Florida today! Over millions of years continents move slowly around the planet at roughly the same speed as fingernails grow.

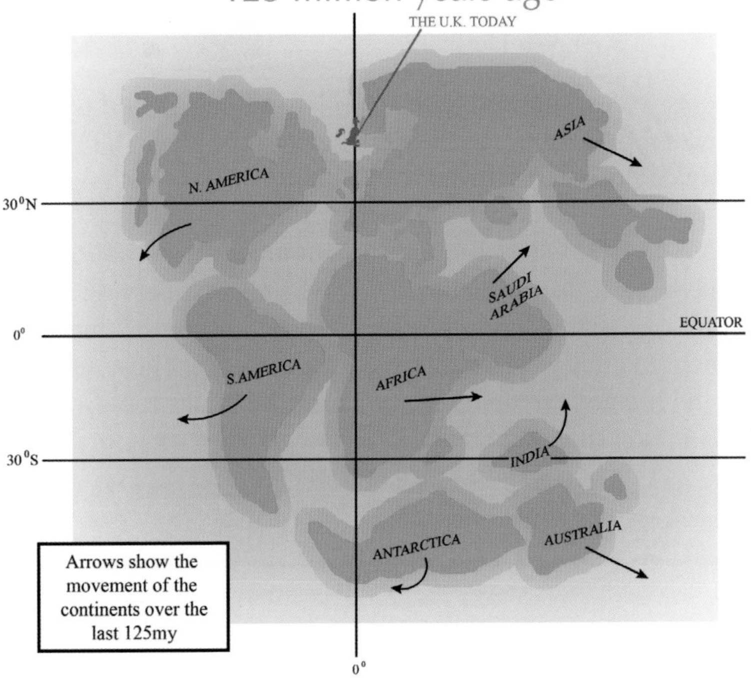

It would have been impossible to recognise the characteristic shape of the Sussex coast in the Lower Cretaceous. Britain was landlocked between North America and Europe in a giant northern continent called Laurasia. The Boreal Sea lay to the north of what is now London and a broad low-lying subtropical plain with rivers, lakes and deltas extended from Dorset to the Isle of Wight, Hampshire, Sussex, Surrey and Kent.

The climate across southern England would have been subtropical with temperatures of around 20 to 24 degrees centigrade throughout the year; probably with seasonal patterns of rainfall. Seasons produce distinctive cycles of sedimentation; the heavy tropical rains cause rivers to flood and in consequence, substantial quantities of gravel and sand are deposited. During periods of drought and low rainfall, rivers flow more slowly and deposit silts and clays. These changing sedimentary patterns can be seen in exposures of rock in streams and in the numerous clay pits across Sussex. Geologists can make judgements on the climate by examining the fossils found in the sedimentary rocks in an area.

The remains of plants known to belong to subtropical flora such as ferns, cycads and horsetail ferns have all been found in local sedimentary rocks. The presence of crocodile and turtle fossils reinforces the hypothesis that the Wealden climate was much warmer than that experienced in South-East England today.

Fossilised sequoia cone found in a clay pit near Horsham

Cycads

The Wealden sediments were deposited in two sub-basins. The Weald Basin is the term used to describe the area covered by Kent, East Sussex and West Sussex. The Wessex Basin covers sediments deposited over Dorset and the Isle of Wight.

Geologically, a basin is an area where sediment accumulates over millions of years. The basin may subside due to faults lowering the floor of the basin, allowing shallow seas to transgress easily across a low-lying landscape and deposit marine sediments. Over time, rivers transport sediment to create deltas and estuarine deposits. These sediments then gradually push back the sea and create new land. Today, similar processes are happening in the River Nile delta and the Mississippi delta.

Geological map of South-East England

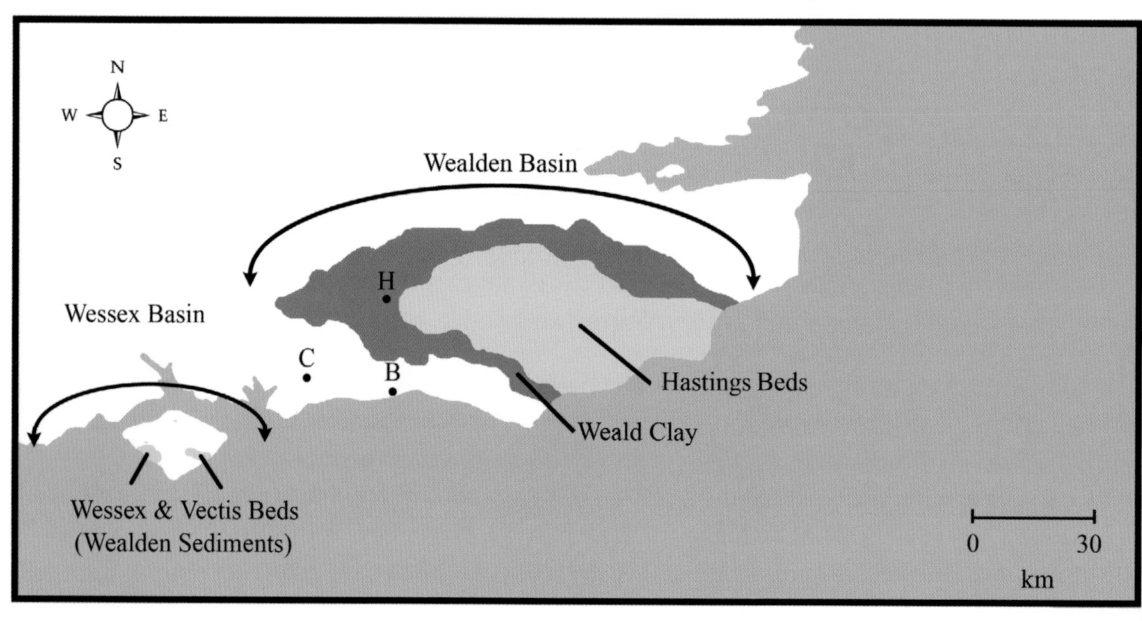

H = Horsham C = Chichester B = Brighton = Weald Clay = Hastings Beds

The Weald Basin accumulated sediment for several millions of years in the Lower Cretaceous period during which time thick deposits of clay built up in lakes and on floodplains. The Wealden sands were deposited typically in rivers, sandbanks, deltas and estuaries. Geologists imagine a picture of slow-moving rivers meandering across a floodplain depositing thin sheets of sand, clay and silt. In times of flood they burst their river channels and erode river banks, submerging floodplains with clay and silty water.

Palaeogeographic map of South East England around 125my showing the deposition of Wealden sediments

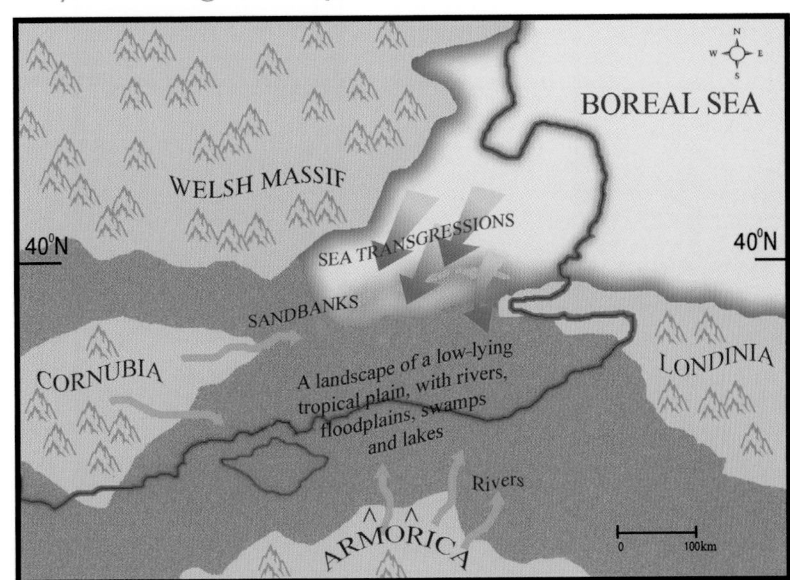

These changing geographical conditions are characteristic of low-lying landscapes and the nature of the environment helps to explain why beds like Horsham Stone are a localised deposit that can vary in thickness and lateral extent.

It is thought that a combination of climate change and uplift of mountains surrounding the Wealden Basin altered the rates of erosion and deposition of sediment. To the west of the Wealden Basin, the Atlantic Ocean was starting to open up and the movement of the Earth's crust caused faults to move and mountain ranges to change their height. This in turn influenced the patterns of rainfall and the prevailing winds. Cycles of deposition can be traced across the Wealden Basin that represent possible changes to topographic barriers that blocked or influenced weather patterns.

The flat nature of the landscape meant that it was relatively easy for the sea to sweep over the land and change the salinity of the rivers and lakes. The variation in the salinity is represented in the fossil record with the presence of the Large and Small 'Paludina' Limestones. The Large 'Paludina' Limestone, Viviparus fluviorum, seemed to prefer freshwater environments, whilst the Small 'Paludina' Limestone, Viviparus infracretacicus, appeared to favour more saline water. The changing geographical environments across the Wealden Basin had a major impact on the distribution of the flora and fauna.

Large 'Paludina' shown as fossil and polished marble section

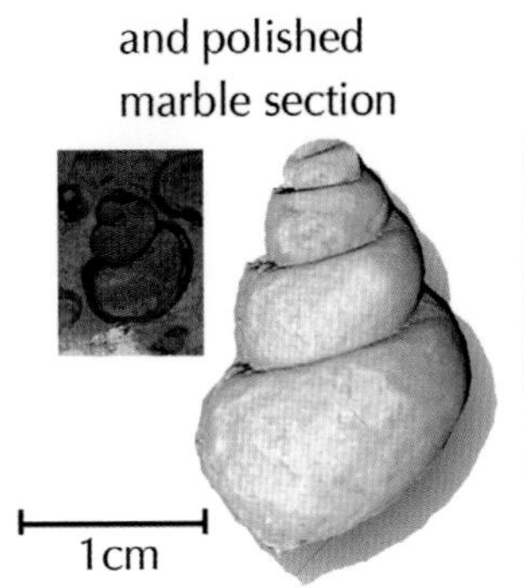

1cm

Small 'Paludina' enlarged from a polished marble section

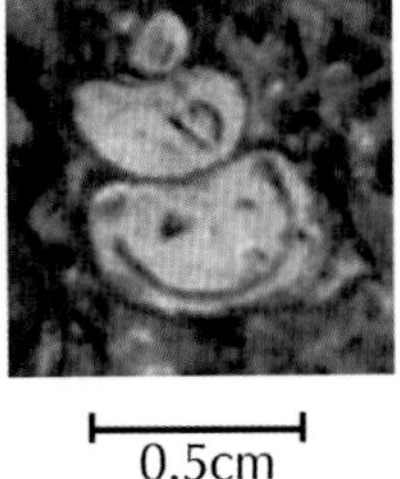

0.5cm

Geological Column of the Lower Cretaceous period

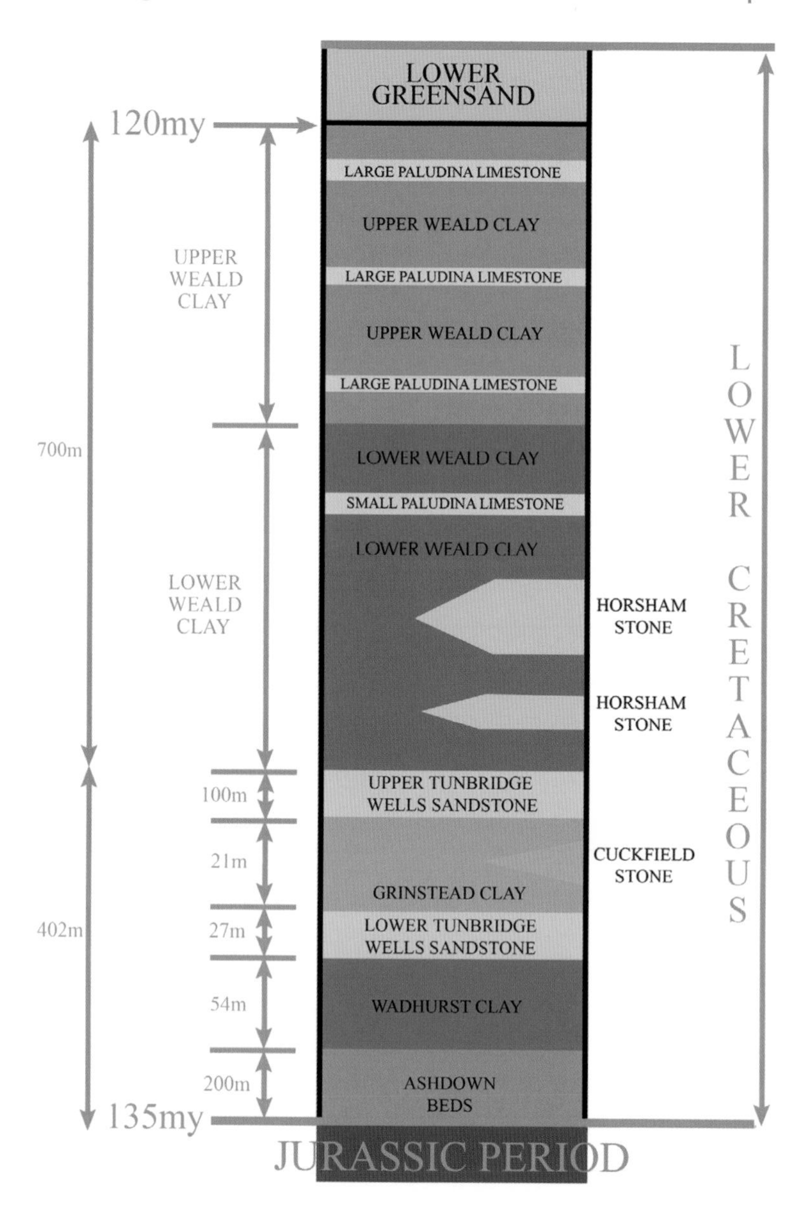

Geological surveys and research over the past 150 years have produced various models of what the Weald looked like over 130 million years ago. The exposures revealed in the many clay pits across the region have provided a wealth of information for the investigating geologist to record and analyse. Although many local clay pits have closed due to the changes in brick-making economics, a number of brick companies near Horsham, Ockley and Cranleigh still have working pits. Fossils and geological samples collected from these sites help geologists to reconstruct the palaeogeography of the Lower Cretaceous period.

The broad concept of the Wealden Basin representing a tropical, low-lying landscape has been well established over the past 100 years. As the science of geology has developed and more research has been carried out, the basic model has been redefined and better understood.

Data collected from one famous local brick pit, Smokejack Quarry at Ockley, has contributed significantly to the understanding of the Wealden sediments. In 1983, a local amateur geologist, William Walker, discovered a large 'claw' in part of the quarry. This was recognised as one of the most important dinosaur discoveries of the last century. It was named Baryonyx walkeri in recognition of the collector. Only 60% of the skeleton was recovered. The dinosaur probably died close to where it was buried after drifting along a river and then coming to rest on a mudflat. A detailed examination of the skeleton shows that some of the bones were broken, possibly as a result of being transported by river currents. Reconstruction of the dinosaur enables palaeontologists to deduce that Baryonyx roamed across the Wealden swamps using its long, powerful claws to catch large freshwater fish such as Lepidotes. Its teeth are straight, rounded and blade-like with minute serrations along the front and back edges, very like those of modern crocodiles. A number of isolated teeth of Baryonyx have been found on the Isle of Wight.

Careful analysis of the strata in Smokejack Quarry and other nearby quarries reveal a wide range of evidence to show the complexity of life in the Wealden Basin. The discovery of many new species of insects has been significant in the understanding of palaeoentomology – the study of fossil insects. Cockroaches, beetles, caddis flies, dragonflies, termites and lacewings have all been found in Weald Clay deposits. Larger fossil finds include pterosaur bones, crocodile scutes and teeth, numerous Iguanodon bones and partial skeletons and turtles. Gastroliths have been found, which are thought to be small, usually rounded stones that were swallowed by dinosaurs to facilitate the breakdown of tough and fibrous vegetation. These stones show signs of etching due to the action of stomach acids in the guts of dinosaurs.

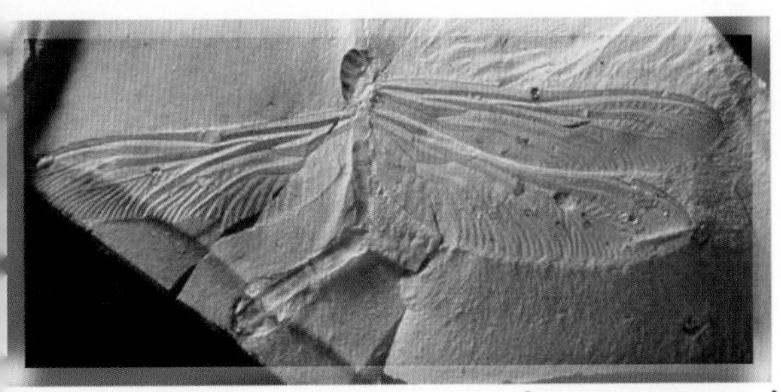

Dragonfly fossil 2cm

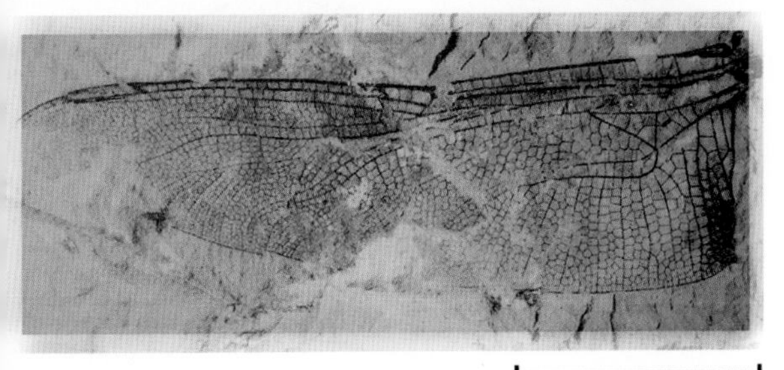

Insect wing 1cm

1cm

Is this a fossil? Possibly a caddis fly case?

actual size

Lepidotes fish scales and fin

All of this evidence is used to reconstruct carefully the ancient landscape across the Wealden Basin. Geologists piece together all the clues in the rocks to build up a detailed picture of the world as it would have been millions of years ago. This reconstruction is callec a palaeoenvironment.

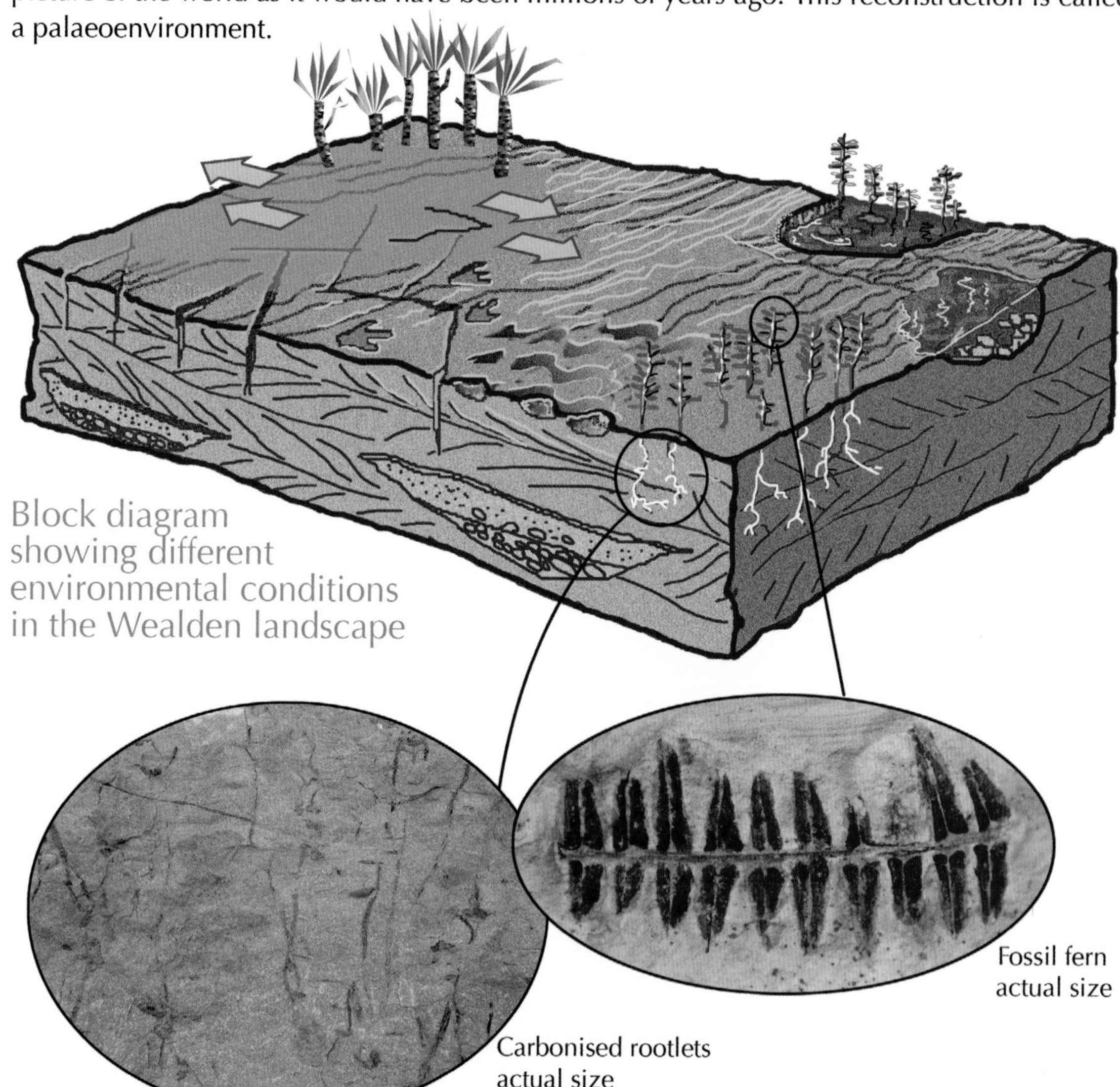

Block diagram showing different environmental conditions in the Wealden landscape

Fossil fern actual size

Carbonised rootlets actual size

Many blocks of Horsham Stone show fossil roots and stems. Some of the plant fossils found look like bamboo. These are Equisetites and are identical almost to the horsetail ferns to be found in ditches and boggy areas across Britain today. These plant fossils indicate therefore swamp or semi-aquatic conditions in the Wealden Basin.

A large number of the stems are preserved in their original vertical life position suggesting that they were fossilised rapidly in their soil horizon. A fossil soil bed has been recorded around Slinfold. This bed of rock was clay once that had been weathered and baked into a mixture of mottled purple and brown sediment whilst it was exposed as a mudflat. During the construction of new houses in Southwater, a number of interesting fossil finds turned up. Sand-filled Equisetites' stems were found in sandstone blocks and are unique in that they allow a three-dimensional fossil to be studied.

Plant debris that accumulates in a swamp tends to be decomposed only partially, owing to the low levels of oxygen allowing a process of carbonation to occur. This results in thin seams or lenses of lignite. Lignite is a form of brown coal that forms from compressed peat. Coal deposits accumulate in a stagnant, anoxic environment where partial decomposition of plant material occurs. These fragments of plant material may be only a few millimetres thin but they give another valuable clue as to the conditions that occurred in the Wealden Basin. Occasionally, fragments of wood and charcoal can be found in the Weald Clay providing clear evidence of forest fires burning across the landscape. During times of prolonged drought, lightning strikes on dead trees. This can start a firestorm and evidence of fires has been revealed in sedimentary layers beneath the Everglades in Florida, long before man inhabited the area.

Fossilised Leaf Hopper wing

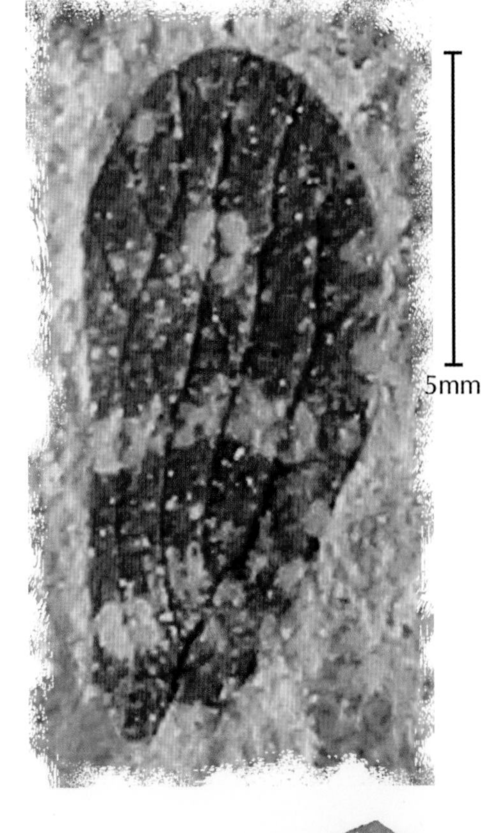

Cast of a dinosaur footprint found in Wealden Sandstone, on the coast near Hastings

Fossil beetles 20mm

'Fossilised' raindrops are rare features. Heavy rainfall falling on wet mud creates the imprints, which are subsequently preserved having been baked by the tropical sun.

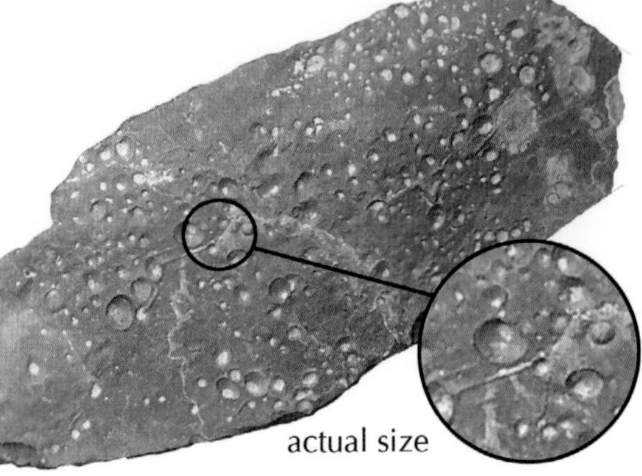

A new quarry near Horsham has revealed some fascinating sedimentary structures. These are features or markings that occur on the bedding planes of the sandstone beds. Desiccation or sun cracks form when the sun bakes wet sediments creating polygonal shrinkage cracks. These cracks are later infilled with silt or clay.

40c

Many species of dinosaur roamed the Wealden floodplains and swamps and left behind their footprints. A number of different species of dinosaur have been found in clay pits across the Weald. Polacanthus rudgwickensis was a significant discovery made recently in a clay pit near Rudgwick. Several other species of dinosaur have been found across the Weald over the past 200 years. A number of local dinosaur finds can be seen in Horsham Museum where a geological display shows a range of fossils that has been collected in the area.

Polacanthus rudgwickensis (reproduced by kind permission of J. Sibbick

Walking across the mudflats and sandbanks were large numbers of dinosaurs. Dinosaur footprints preserved as moulds and casts have been found across the Weald for over 250 years. Dr Gideon Mantell was one of the early geologists who lived in Sussex in the 1800's. One day in the spring of 1822, Mary Mantell was with her husband on a visit to a patient near the village of Faygate. While he was with the patient, she went for a walk in Tilgate Forest and saw a pile of stones that was being used by roadmen to repair a road. Instantly, she recognised some unusual teeth in the rocks and picked up the fossils and showed them to her husband. These finds were to become one of the most important events in the scientific study of dinosaurs. In 1834, Gideon Mantell published a description of the find and named the animal Iguanodon, which means 'iguana tooth'.Throughout the 1800's significant dinosaur finds were made across Sussex and Kent. Maidstone has the Iguanodon in its coat of arms as a tribute to the major dinosaur finds of the early 1800's.

Dinosaur bones on display at Horsham Museum

Baryonyx walkeri (reproduced by kind permission of J. Sibbick)

Iguanodon and young wandering across the Wealden landscape (reproduced by kind permission of J. Sibbick)

The wide range of geological evidence indicates clearly that West Sussex was a vastly different place 130 million years ago. The fossils show that there was a great diversity of life living on the broad, flat subtropical landscape. There is a great debate today about global warming and there is no doubt that our climate in Britain is undergoing changes. Carbon dioxide and other greenhouse gases are being released by human activity. It is startling to realise that back in the Cretaceous period, carbon dioxide levels in the atmosphere are estimated at being over 700ppm, compared with current levels of 340ppm. Many geologists talk of the Cretaceous 'hot house effect'. This was a time in the Earth's history when the whole planet was several degrees warmer than today; the poles did not have ice sheets and sea levels were rising rapidly. Towards the end of the Cretaceous period, around 90 million years ago, most of Britain would have been submerged beneath a deep, tropical sea that was depositing chalk.

The sediments of the Wealden Basin were buried under hundreds of metres of sediment over the next 100 million years and were then uplifted gradually by continental plate movements. Slowly, erosion and weathering would expose the Wealden rocks. The geological landscape of Sussex would have been revealed gradually around 40 million years ago. Approximately 2 million years ago, the Ice Age began and glaciers started to sweep across Britain, travelling as far south as a line from London to Bristol. Sussex experienced an arctic climate of permafrost, thin snow cover and short cool summers. The profile of the South and North Downs and the low scarp edge produced by the Horsham Stone would have been visible to the early human settlers as the Ice Age melted away around 12,000 years ago. West Sussex has experienced tremendous changes since the Lower Cretaceous period!

5 A LOOK INSIDE HORSHAM STONE

Horsham Stone is a series of thin, calcareous sandstones that are found in the lower parts of the Weald Clay. Two distinctive main ripple-marked beds can be identified and can be traced across several kilometres around Horsham. These are the beds that have been worked over the centuries for roofing and flagstones. There are a number of other thin sandstone beds that occur close to the main seam and these beds tended to be used for walling and foundations. These different sandstone beds range from 3cm to 15cm in thickness. The sandstone is a very hard, well-cemented rock that can be split easily along thin layers or bedding planes. These natural characteristics have made it attractive to builders for hundreds of years.

A close look at a fresh piece of Horsham Stone reveals tiny, flaky, sparkling minerals called mica. Other 'sugar grained' minerals are quartz. A consistent feature of the stone is that it has an even grain size, which means that virtually all mineral grains of sand are the same size. These grains are held together by a calcareous cement that creates a tough, resistant rock. A study of buildings across Sussex shows how well the Horsham Stone roofs and walls have stood the test of time and many Horsham slates have been reused over hundreds of years.

Section through Horsham Stone

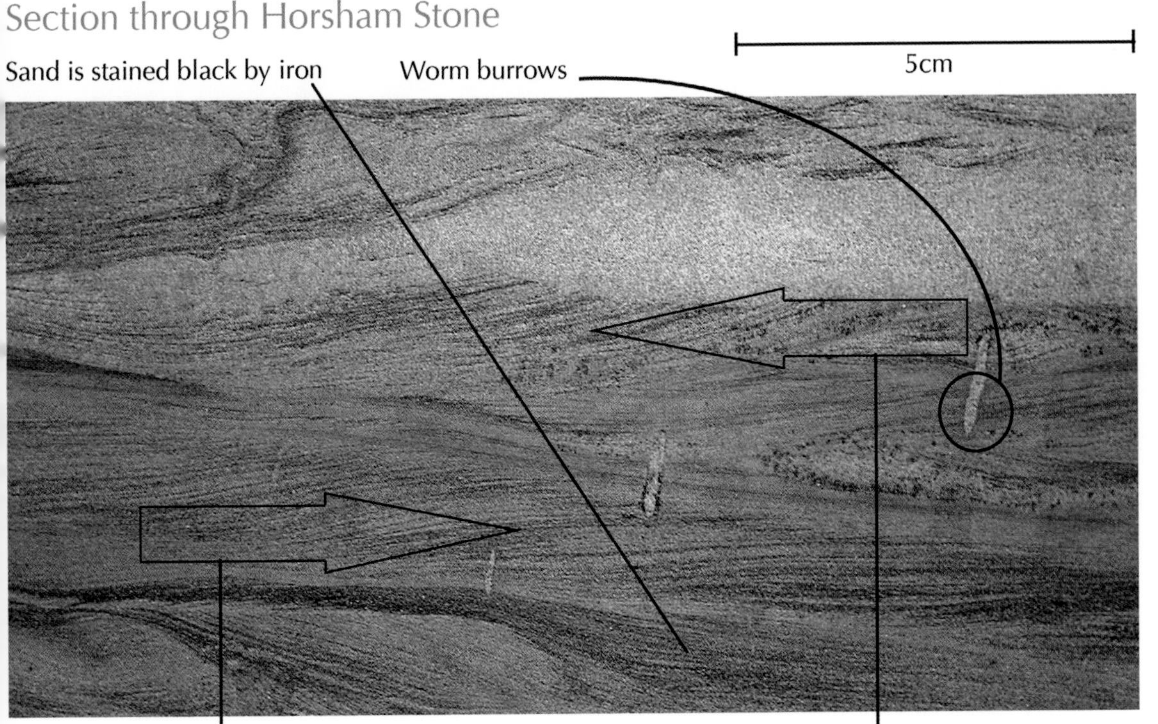

The main stone seams are just below ground level; for example, near Broadbridge Heath it i only 2m deep. For hundreds of years farmers to the south of Horsham could simply dig shallow pits in fields and excavate the stone. Today, field names still show the extent of these workings with names like 'Stonefield', 'Stone Pit Wood' and 'Stone Barn'.

When the Horsham bypass was being constructed in 1974, massive slabs of Horsham Stone were excavated; some slabs were over 12m across. Many of these slabs were found near the Hop Oast roundabout. More recently, large slabs have been dug up in Southwater as new houses have been built.

View of the bypass under construction

When exposed as a fresh slab, the stone is a golden yellow colour which weathers gradually to a darker brown tint. Traditionally, the prized pieces of stone were the rippled ones. These were used for their 'anti-slip' property and in the early eighteenth century the stones were described as 'furrowed and wrinkled surfaces that are ideal for paving and pathways'.

Slab of rippled Horsham Stone

Section of Horsham Stone showing ripple marks

A wide range of sedimentary structures can be found on the tops of the sandstone slabs. These are features and varying patterns that are left in the sand by the action of water currents. Horsham Stone is famous for its many beautiful and intricate ripple marks.

Slab of Horsham Stone showing sole marks at the top and ripple marks at the bottom

The geological story behind the ripples is fascinating. Anyone who has walked around Chichester Harbour or on any sandy beach at low tide will have seen ripple marks. Ripples are made when gentle water currents move grains of sand slowly along a beach or sandbank. Tidal currents or river currents all produce ripples. The key point to look at with Horsham Stone ripples is their symmetry. Close study will show some ripples to be symmetrical; that is each side of the ripple crest has a slope of the same angle. This indicates that the water currents were moving backwards and forwards sweeping the grains of sand into a symmetrical profile. These conditions can occur when tides ebb and flow across a beach or when river currents gently meander back and forth in the shallows.

Sawn cross-section through symmetrical ripple marks

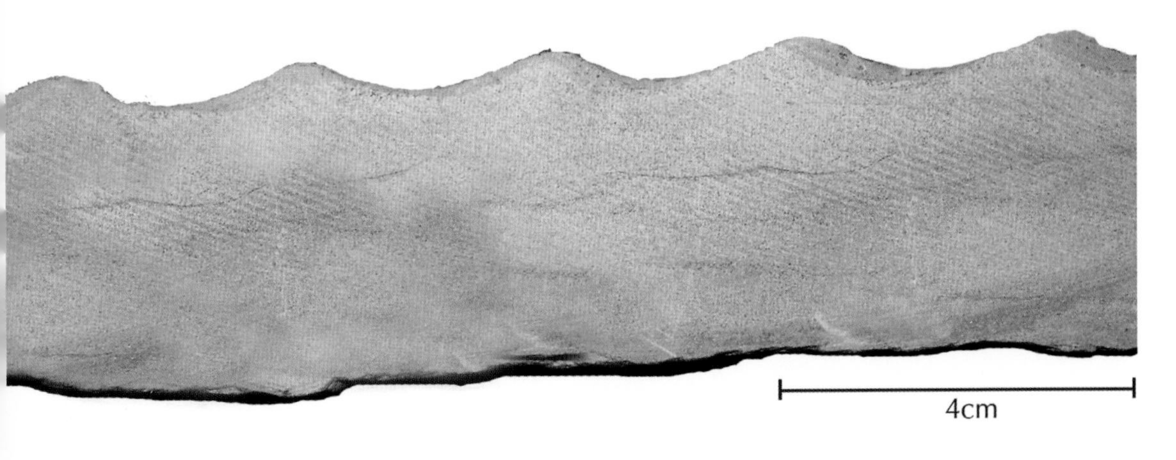

The height of the ripples varies. The normal range is between 5mm and 2cm and this would suggest changing speeds of water. The crests of some ripples run parallel with each other and some crests show a twisting, sinuous crest line. Occasionally, the crest may split into two and this is called a bifurcating crest. All these subtle ripple patterns tell us that the water currents were changing their direction of flow and their speed. This is typical of sediments being swept along in shallow rivers or estuaries.

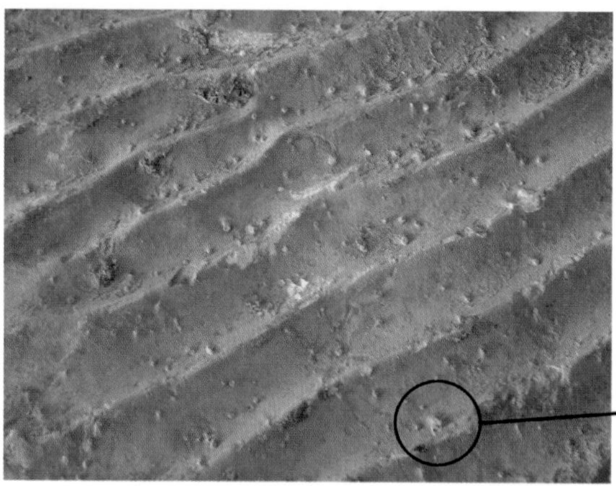

Trace fossils can be formed by organisms crawling across a mudflat or sandbank. Very often burrows can be seen in Horsham sandstone. Worm burrows are quite common on ripple-marked surfaces. As worms moved through the sediment, they would come to the surface and leave small, circular marks, which are often preserved standing proud of the ripple's surface.

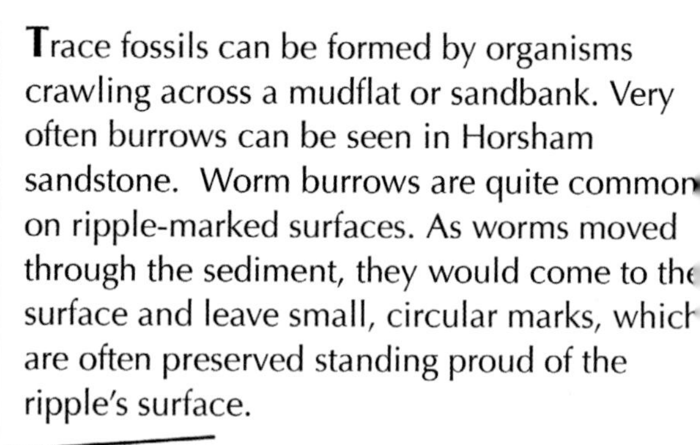

Sole marks which look like saucer-shaped depressions are a range of features produced by faster, turbulent water currents. They can be 1cm to 3cm deep and up to 20cm across. They show that the water currents were colliding and swirling around and in effect, scouring out the sandy river bed.

This massive slab of Horsham Stone is over 8m long. It shows exceptional detail of several different types of ripple marks. In the foreground are flat-topped ripples. These then merge into more sinuous crested ripples. These ripples represent probably a shallow water sandbank over which different water currents were flowing in a Wealden river.

Some ripples have their crests eroded, creating a flat-topped ripple. Ripple patterns can change suddenly even on a small paving slab. There are plenty of ripple marks to see on the pavement along the Causeway in Horsham. A visit to many of the older pubs around the town will show the spectacular variation in patterns. Good examples can be seen at The George and Dragon Pub at Dragons Green and The Black Horse in Nuthurst. Why not have a relaxing drink and a chat about the geology beneath your feet?

Some ripples are asymmetrical in their profile. One side has a shallow slope and the other a steeper one. This indicates that the water current was flowing up along the shallow side and over the crest, causing the sand grains to slip down the steeper slope. In this steady movement, ripples migrate down current, showing the current direction. When slabs are cut to size for paving or roofing, the detailed internal structure of the sand grains can be seen clearly. Often, they show a pattern of cross-bedding, indicating that currents changed their direction during deposition. This was due possibly to sandbanks migrating and blocking the flow of water, or changes in the wind direction causing water currents to flow from a new direction.

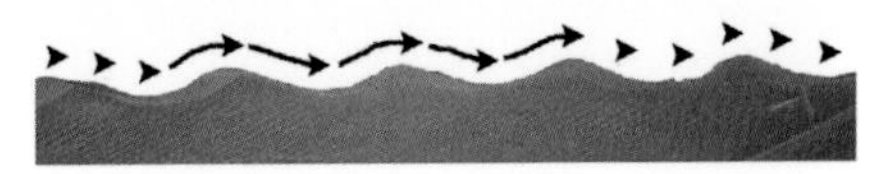

The current moved left to right on this photograph taken at Chichester Harbour; the steeper slope is shown in shadow.

Ladder ripples are quite rare in that they have two sets of ripples that have formed at right angles to each other. The larger ripple is formed by a dominant current. The second ripple forms in the trough at right angles to the main ripple and is smaller. The sand to make the smaller ripple is gently swept off the larger ripples. Water currents that change direction within a tidal cycle or are changed by the wind can form these unusual ripple marks.

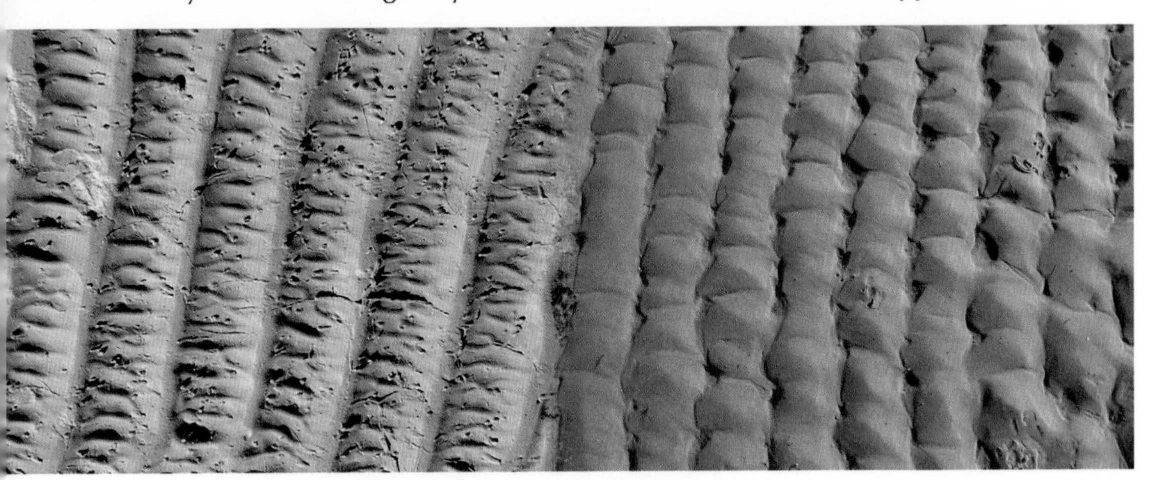

Ladder ripples in Horsham Stone | Present day ladder ripples

Any dinosaur or insect that walks across these drying surfaces will leave behind footprints or tail prints. Geologists call these types of fossils trace fossils. They can be as small as 2mm and range up to 70cm when formed by dinosaurs! Dinosaur footprints have been found in many clay pits and quarries over the past 200 years, although footprints are still unrecorded in Horsham Stone. Footprints can be preserved as casts or moulds. The most common dinosaur footprint found in Sussex belongs to the Iguanodon, an example of which we see here.

We can see worm casts on sandy beaches at low tide all around the British Isles. Worms burrow through the sand and filter out organic particles. They eject undigested particles in the familiar twisted tube pattern. This specimen was photographed on a slab of Horsham Stone.

One common form of trace fossil, which looks like a sinuous tube running across a bedding plane, often for several metres, is Beaconites. It is thought to have been made by a shrimp or worm-like organism.

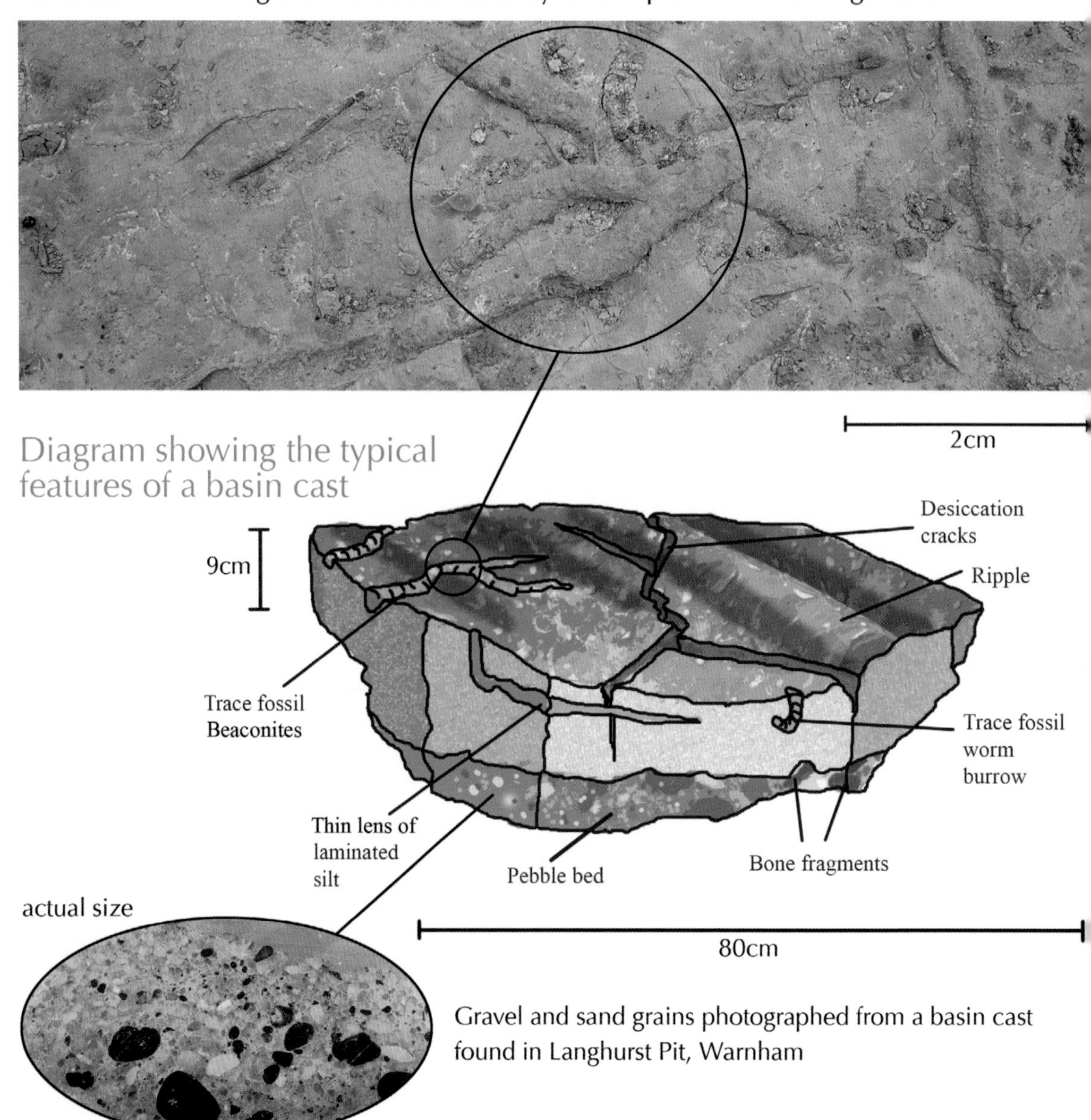

Diagram showing the typical features of a basin cast

Gravel and sand grains photographed from a basin cast found in Langhurst Pit, Warnham

Some Horsham Stone slabs show unusual curved patterns on a bedding plane. These patterns are horizontal sections worn down on to trough cross-bedding. Trough cross-bedding forms when turbulent water swirls around and piles up short, steep-sided ripple-like structures with deep troughs. The fast flowing water is constantly eroding and depositing sand in a changing pattern with the result that ripples migrate over each other and reveal a cross-bedding pattern when viewed in cross-section. The curved surface viewed on the slabs shows the direction of the migrating and slumping ripple. There are some excellent examples of this structure on the paving slabs along the Causeway and in Pump Alley, just off the Causeway in Horsham.

Trough Cross-Bedding in Horsham Stone

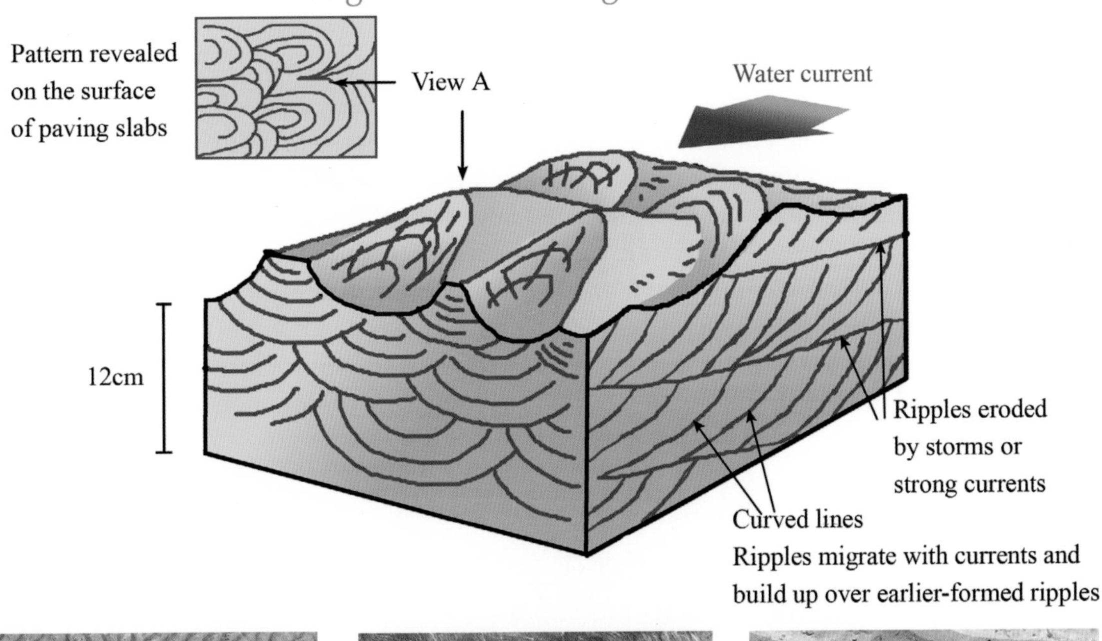

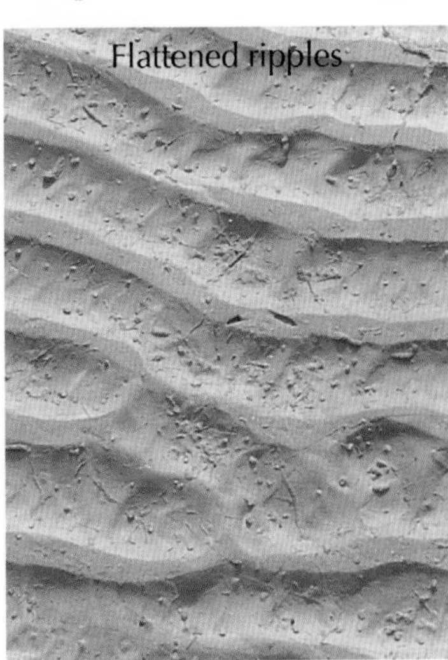

The geological detail preserved in Horsham Stone is remarkable. It must be remembered that most of the original features that were formed 130 million years ago were eroded by tides or strong currents and, exceptionally, some of these features were preserved (by a measure of geological good fortune) for us to study and wonder at today.

6 A LOOK INSIDE SUSSEX MARBLE

The name Sussex Marble covers two types of limestone: the Large and Small 'Paludina' Limestone. A third type of limestone can be found also in the Weald Clay. This is the 'Cyrena' Limestone. This rock has never been used as an ornamental marble but can be found in stream beds or in walls as rubble infill.

The Large 'Paludina' Limestone

The geological record shows four distinct Large 'Paludina' beds with a number of other beds that do not have the same continuity across East and West Sussex. There is one distinct bed of the Small 'Paludina' Limestone but numerous other thin seams can be found exposed in stream beds and clay pits across East and West Sussex. In Warnham clay pit several Small 'Paludina' beds and 'Cyrena' Limestone beds have been recorded. Some of the better known exposures of the Sussex Marble have tended to be in South Surrey and North-West Sussex. Places like Petworth, Northchapel, Charlwood and Kirdford were important areas of extraction for hundreds of years. Where the limestone layers occur close to the surface, they can be observed in stream beds and degraded road cuttings, and farmers can easily plough up blocks.

Flooded 19th century Sussex Marble pit, north of Charlwood and a small block of Large 'Paludina' Limestone

12cm

The Large 'Paludina' Limestone was the rock that was quarried traditionally for its decorative properties. Some of the thickest seams found in West Sussex occurred around Newdigate and Charlwood.

The 'Paludina' Limestone is actually a highly fossiliferous rock. It is made up almost entirely of whole or fragmentary Viviparus fluviorum. This is a gastropod that lived in shallow freshwater conditions, such as lakes, oxbow lakes and marsh environments. The fossil shells are mixed in with a range of sediments, usually fine sand, silt or clay and millions of microscopic fossils called ostracods, which are very similar to water fleas. Fine-grained sediments like silt and clay suggest that the water currents were slow-moving or stationary and the abundance of large, sometimes broken shells, suggests turbulent water currents. This conflicting evidence probably indicates that the fossil material was subjected to a number of changing conditions before finally coming to rest in a river or shellbank.

Polished section of Large 'Paludina' Sussex Marble

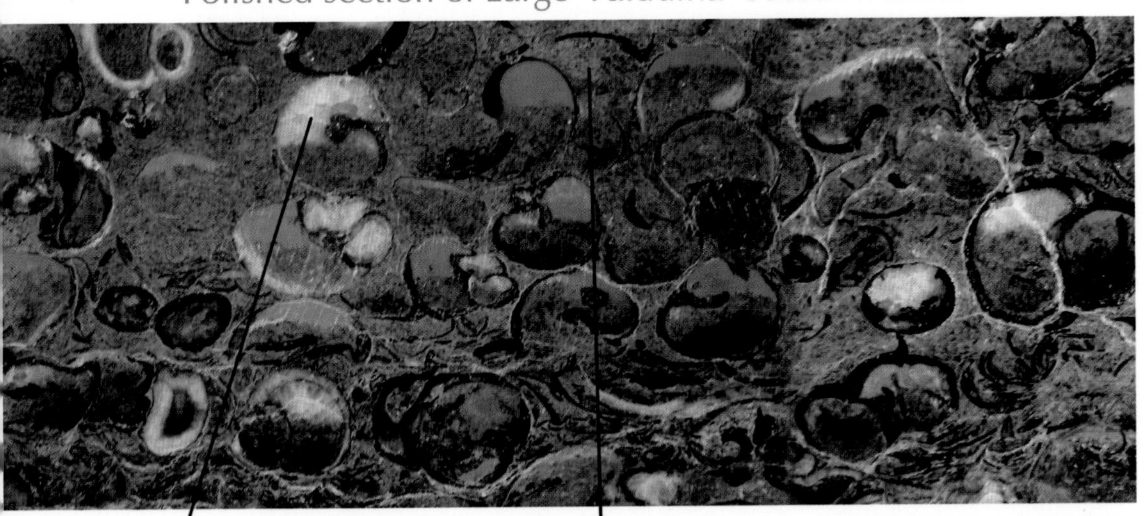

White calcite can be seen inside some of the gastropod shells

The matrix is pale brown silt

actual size

Close analysis of polished sections reveals a range of interesting details. Many shells have all their internal spaces infilled with white calcite. This mineral probably migrated into the empty shell millions of years after burial. Some shells are only half filled with mud or silt. During burial by a flood or storm, the shells would have been rolled around and sediment only partially managed to penetrate the inner whorls of the shell. Later, migration of calcite filled the remaining space of the inner coil or whorls of the shell. This process created what geologists call a geopetal infill. The shells do not show any real pattern or orientation and this suggests that the shells were thrown together in large concentrations or 'coquinas'. 'Coquinas' are massive deposits of shells washed up by storms and concentrated into long linear deposits on beaches. Today, similar shell concentrations can be seen along the North Kent coast which is famous for its oyster shell beds washed up on beaches. One current interpretation of the 'Paludina' Limestone is that it represents a similar geological process along an ancient lake shoreline.

Some of the Large 'Paludina' contains also other fossil remains. Fish teeth and fish scales can be seen in some polished pieces. In rough-cut blocks in the walls of Warminghurst Church are the occasional scales of Lepidotes, a large, carp like freshwater fish whose fossil remains are frequently found throughout the Wealden sediments. Other unusual fossil finds in limestone are the teeth and spines of a freshwater shark belonging to the species Hybodus.

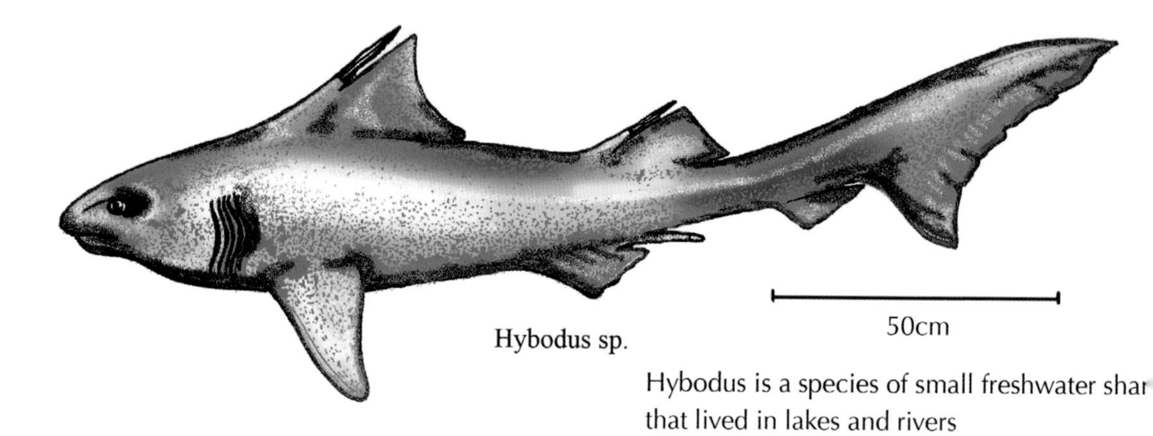

Hybodus is a species of small freshwater shar
that lived in lakes and rivers

Diagram of a typical lake floor environment showing a large carp-like Lepidotes

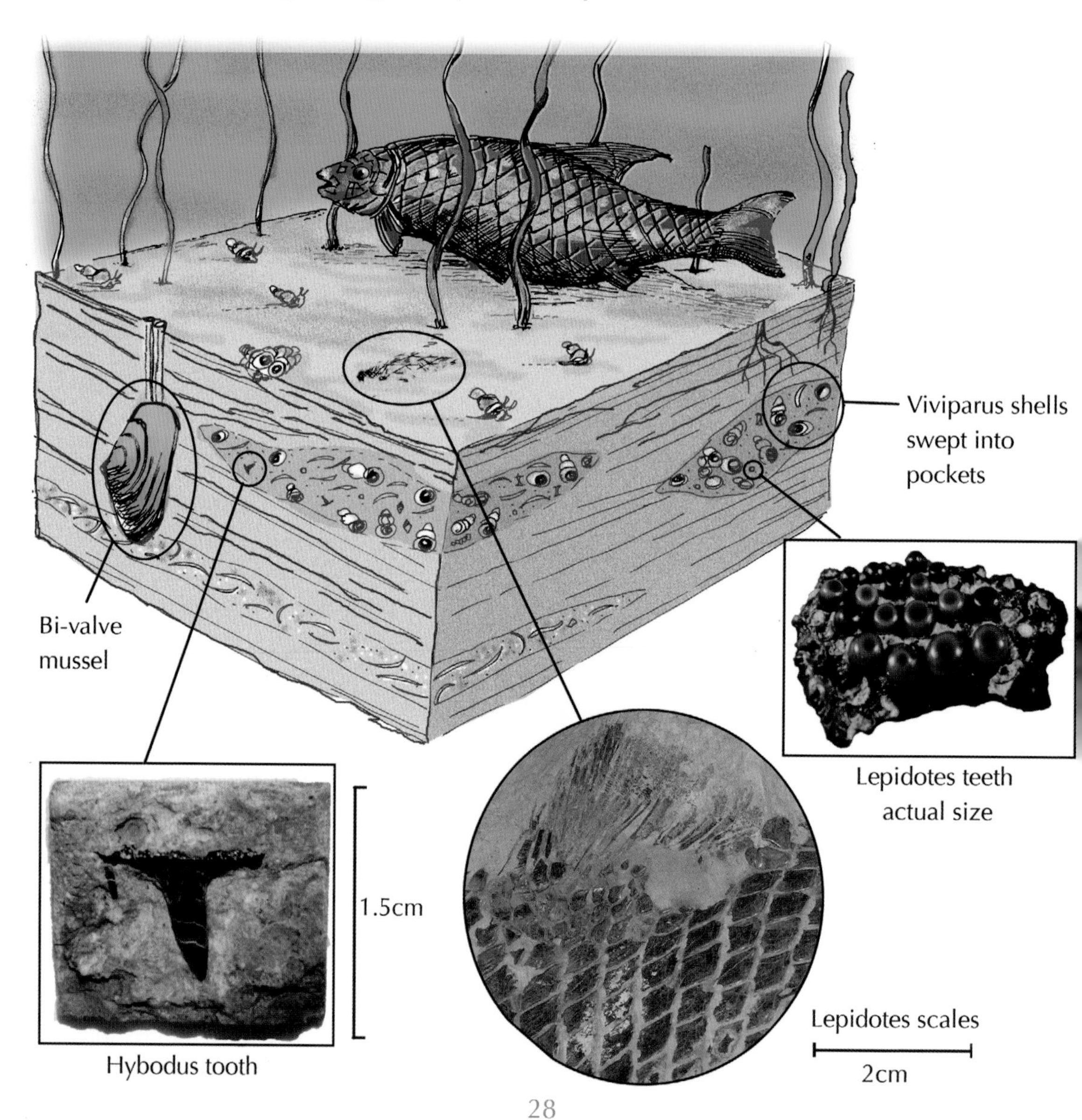

Fragments of freshwater mussel can be found mixed in with the snail shells. The fossils may show some winnowing action by water current which occurs when oscillating water currents orientate the broken shells in lines or layers. A study of the polished sections of the marble reveals many beautiful patterns of fossils.

Ostracods have been found in the matrix around the shells. Ostracods are small-scaled fossils which range in size from the microscopic to a few millimetres. They are the skeletal remains of tiny water fleas that once lived in the freshwater environments across the Wealden delta. These fossils have been very useful in correlating the Lower Cretaceous sediments across the South of England.

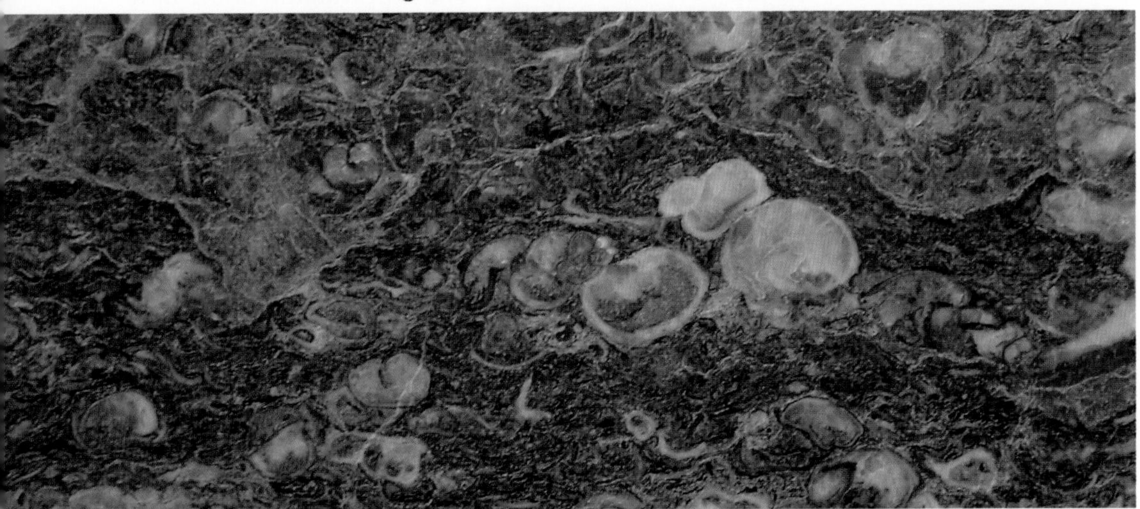

actual size

The rounded, globular shape of Viviparus fluviorum made it particularly robust. Polished mantelpieces and church fonts show dozens of complete shells, usually distinctive with their polished, white, calcite infill.

The toughness of the shell meant that very often it would weather out of its matrix in the limestone which created a weakness in the stone when used as an external building material. A number of churches in Sussex have Large 'Paludina' slabs in porches, steps and lych-gates such as those at Kirdford Church. Provided that the worst of the weather was kept at bay, the limestone survived and made an attractive feature polished by the feet of churchgoers. Several steps leading up to Thakeham Church are made of the Large 'Paludina' Limestone.

The Norman tub font at Poling Church, near Arundel
The inside is lined with lead

Section of the wall at Warminghurst Church

10cm

Warminghurst Church shows a superb example of rough-cut Sussex Marble being used in buttresses and walls. The weathered side of the church shows the shells in various stages of being etched out of their matrix and shells that have fallen out of the rock can be seen scattered on the ground.

The construction of the new Billingshurst bypass revealed excellent sections through the Wealden sediments, where seams of the Large 'Paludina' Limestone were exposed. Coneyhurst Common, to the east of Billingshurst, shows a small overgrown road section of the Large 'Paludina'. It is possible to use the Horsham Geological Map to trace the seams of 'Paludina' Limestone across the landscape. Slight topographic changes from Billingshurst to Ashington show the effect of the limestone on the evolution of the Sussex landscape.

There are a number of thin Sussex Marble seams that run around the Weald Clay outcrop. Sussex Marble is located characteristically just above the Horsham Stone beds and numerous thin seams are found as discontinuous beds that may be traced for a kilometre or less. Seams of the marble run across West Sussex into East Sussex and one particular seam can be traced across the Western Weald for over 15km. The seams are usually around 6cm to 9cm thick, the thicker seams being followed carefully by quarrymen. Because the Small 'Paludina' has a weaker structure and was found in thinner steams, it was rarely used. Small tomb slabs and edging pieces can be seen in churches.

The Small 'Paludina' Limestone

As its name suggests, the Small 'Paludina' is a slightly smaller gastropod than the Large 'Paludina'. It has been recorded in a number of localities that the limestone shows desiccation cracks, indicating that the muddy sediment mixed around the pockets of shells of the Small 'Paludina' dried out and developed shrinkage cracks. Calcite infills many of the shells and mud and silt are the main matrix. Polished sections of this limestone show varying patterns of winnowing action suggesting that the shells had been transported by variable water speeds. Fragments of freshwater bivalves do occur in the shell matrix.

7 THE HISTORY OF THE USE OF HORSHAM STONE

One of the earliest records of the use of Horsham Stone is at Amberley Mount on the South Downs, above the village of Amberley. This is where archaeologists have found 14 quern fragments made of Horsham Stone dating to the late Bronze Age.

Mesolithic sites around Horsham tend to be clustered on higher, well-drained ground, where ridges and crest lines provided a suitable vantage point and defensive site. Horsham Stone is an aquifer that releases pure spring water and there are a number of small springs that emerge along the base of the Horsham Stone crescent-shaped scarp, for example Denne Hill, Rusper Hill and Sedgewick Park. Horsham Stone is a calcareous sandstone which attracts lime-loving algae and lichens to its weathered surface. Roofing slates and tombstones have a distinct biodiversity of lichens growing on their surfaces. As the stone is weathered lime is released from the rock, creating a calcium-rich surface.

Horsham Stone started to be quarried on a more economic basis during the Roman period. Villas such as Bignor and Fishbourne have got examples of Horsham 'slates' and floor slabs. Horsham Stone is a very valuable building stone because it occurs close to the surface and can be split into strong, durable, thin slabs and slates.

Sussex lacks large quantities of suitable building stone, unlike many other counties such as Yorkshire, Derbyshire and Cornwall, so the Roman eye recognised quickly the potential of Horsham Stone as suitable building material.

The suitability and value of Horsham Stone as a building stone was clear to the Romans and there are several examples in West Sussex of its being used in roads and villas. At Bignor Villa, nestling beneath the South Downs, Horsham Stone was cut into triangular-shaped roofing tiles, each fixed with an iron nail at the apex. A number of excavations at Bignor between 1985 -1990 revealed Horsham Stone slabs that were rounded and smoothed on one surface; these were probably used as hearthstones.

The development of buildings in the South-East of England is dominated by the early use of timber-framed structures. The extensive deposits of clay across the Weald meant that from the nineteenth century onwards bricks and tiles quickly became the major building materials. Horsham Stone is not a natural roofing stone compared with other rock types such as slate, millstone grit and Cotswold stone. It is a heavy stone that requires massive timbers in the roof; indeed it must have been difficult to lay them. Often roofs collapsed over time and the stone had to be re-laid. In spite of this, most houses of any consequence in the Weald that were built before the eighteenth century were 'healed' with Horsham Stone.

Historical references refer to delves. These were the actual shallow stone pits from which Horsham stone was extracted.

A number of dressed Horsham Stone roofing slates, found during excavations at Bignor Roman Villa

The area around Fishbourne, near Chichester, was clearly important to the Romans. The Chichester estuary provided an ideal sheltered port for ships, especially for the transport of building materials along the Channel coast. One kilometre to the south of the famous Fishbourne Palace, a number of buildings have been shown to have Horsham Stone tiles and rough paving slabs. A large quantity of tiles has been found at a Romano-British site on Bosham Creek.

A Roman station at Alfoldean, at the junction of the Horsham to Guildford road (A281) and Stane Street (A29), reveals another early example of Horsham Stone being used for a range of constructional purposes. Stane Street was an important Roman road running from the River Thames near London to Chichester and the coast. The Roman station or staging post seemed to have been occupied from around AD 69 to AD 360. The excavations revealed a square-shaped area of occupation with a number of stone-floored buildings, and Stane Street ran straight through the middle of the station. The floors of the buildings varied in their construction; some were 25-30cm thick with hard packed earth and red clay overlaid with iron-stained sandstone slabs. On top of the slabs were bricks or tiles. Other floors consisted o compacted earth with strong, local sandstone laid edgewise and with red bricks and tiles lai in between. A number of paths or service roads also were exposed, running across the station and these had rubble bases with a mixture of gravel, flint and chert. Chert is a flint-like rock that comes from the Lower Greensand beds. This could have come from the Leith Hill area or from near Storrington and Fittleworth. Further excavations on the River Aru at Alfoldean showed that a Roman bridge had been constructed across the river. Various building materials were found in the sediments and in the adjacent river bank.
Horsham Stone slabs and rough blocks were found concentrated mainly in the middle of the river suggesting that the central span of the bridge collapsed, dropping the stone in the deep part of the river. In 1809, a number of timbers and a square-shaped sandstone block were given to Horsham Museum. Much of the remaining stone from the bridge probably was removed over hundreds of years and used in nearby buildings.

Horsham Stone slabs were found laid along Stane Street as it ran through the main area of the staging post. This paving is a symbol of status and indicates clearly that this area was under Roman occupation and control. The site is located close to the River Arun floodplain and some parts of the Roman road were found to have Horsham stone slabs, to provide a firm road base on potentially boggy ground.

Just north of Alfoldean the Roman road branches; one road leads North-West towards Ewhurst, the other North-East towards Ockley. During the Great Storm of 1987, trees were blown down in Nags Wood just south of Ewhurst Green and the newly exposed tree roots ripped up Horsham Stone slabs that were once part of the Roman branch road.

The River Arun flows over the western edge of the Horsham Stone outcrop, near the village of Slinfold. It is possible that the Romans transported stone along the river in small barges, although it is hard to know how navigable the river was in Roman times. Horsham Stone is found in buildings around Chichester Harbour at Bosham and Fishbourne and it seems reasonable to assume that the easiest way to transport stone was down the River Arun to Arundel and Littlehampton, and then along the coast to Chichester Harbour.

Further evidence of Roman use of Horsham Stone comes from a small brick and tile works located at Baystone, near Itchingfield. This consisted of a number of small buildings that were used to make bricks and tiles. Horsham paving slabs have been found around the sides of the building and analysis of the rubble wall debris suggests that Horsham sandstone blocks were being used in the construction of the buildings. Horsham Stone occurs under the low hill on which Itchingfield is located and blocks of stone are commonly found in streams and in fields all over this area.

1922 photograph of excavations in a Roman tile works at Baystone, near Itchingfield.

The use of place names has helped in tracing the use of Horsham Stone. Stammerham is an Anglo-Saxon name meaning settlement by a stone quarry. Christ's Hospital occupies now the site of Stammerham. Throughout the medieval period and up to the eighteenth century this area was clearly a major source of Horsham Stone. Historical records mention regularly stone workings around Stammerham, the value of the stone for building and actual prices for new and second-hand stone. Abandoned open pits are still recognisable around the north of Christ's Hospital. Anglo-Saxons would have used Horsham Stone in the construction of churches and important buildings as it was one of only a few suitable building stones in North Sussex. Evidence for this use can be seen in churches like Sompting and Wiggonholt, near Pulborough. Many Anglo-Saxon churches and buildings would have been demolished for building materials during the Norman period.

Early 19th century tithe map

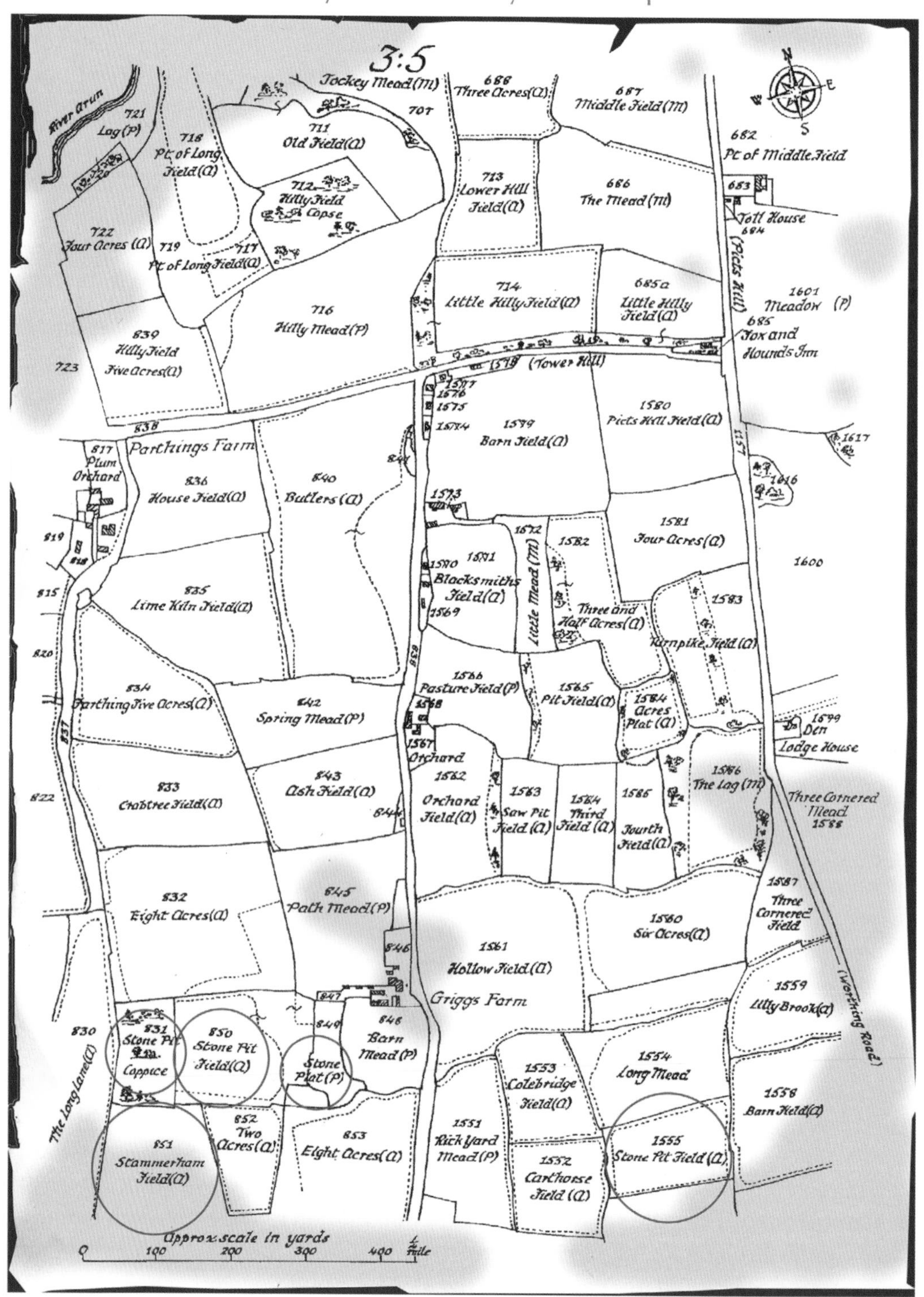

Tithe maps, like the example above, give evidence as to the early workings of the stone. The Worthing Road can be seen running along the right-hand edge of the map. The Fox and Hounds pub now is the Boar's Head pub. Stone Pit Field, Stone Barn, Stonyhurst and Stone Pit Wood are quite common names around Horsham. The pattern of these names indicates that farmers and landowners were digging shallow pits and lifting out the sandstone slabs from a delve at a depth of about 3m or less.

A number of Saxon and Norman Churches have examples of Horsham Stone in their fabric. Sompting Church and Wiggonholt Church have good examples of the stone. Over the centuries churches fell into poor repair and continually were being enlarged. Horsham Stone would have provided an ideal building and roofing material. Very often, tombstones carved out of Horsham Stone were used as floor slabs inside a church.

From Anglo-Saxon times to early Tudor times stone would have been extracted from local, shallow pits and used in a variety of foundations, drainage channels, stone floors and steps. A trackway at Sharpenhurst, near Christ's Hospital has been shown to have small slabs tilted at an angle to create a 'cobble' effect. Near to Stakers Farm, Southwater a clapper bridge has been recorded using large Horsham Stone slabs on the upper surface and stone rubble around the base. A former trackway leading from the bridge has been excavated to reveal grit and pebbles in the foundations with Horsham Stone on top. In addition, some Tudor glass slag was found mixed in with the foundations, which could have been part of an old ridgeway system running from Chesworth to Sedgewick.

When extracted from the ground, Horsham Stone occurs as seams and slabs of various thicknesses. The thinner slabs were easier to split and use for roofing but despite this, the size and weight of the tiles were immense and it required an elaborate and carefully structured timber roof to support the massive load. The thicker slabs were often used as a firm, flat foundation on which to place the major oak timbers. These stones gave a high degree of support and stability on the unstable Weald Clay. The builders at this time must have been well aware of the problems of expansion and contraction of Weald Clay as a result of seasonal changes in the water table. The thick slabs of stone were used also as damp-proof courses. Once quarried, the stone was left exposed to the weather to harden and the winter frost helped with the splitting of the rock. Smaller rubble stone was used for a range of wall filling, foundation material, drainage and, when pulverised, for brick making.

This 18th century print shows a timber-framed house roofed with Horsham Stone. The house can be seen today at the corner of Denne Road and Brighton Road in Horsham.

Horsham Stone is much heavier than thatch, clay tile and the thinner Jurassic slates used in the Cotswolds. The plentiful supply of mature oak across the Weald enabled the development of the famous timber-framed buildings. From the thirteenth century to the mid-sixteenth century, houses were constructed based on a box frame design with massive timber rafters for support. The wealthier yeomen, merchants and farmers had the finance to be able to afford these superb medieval buildings. The roofing slates were fixed onto the rafters by drilling a small hole and using bone fragments, oak pegs or nails. Often the slates were laid on a bed of moss because of the uneven surface of the slates. Over time the nails perished causing slippage and frost penetrated some of the more fissile or cleaved slates. Generally, as can be seen all around the region, Horsham Stone will defy the elements and last for hundreds of years. It is the wooden rafters that fail first. Horsham slates can be re-laid several times and this explains why always there has been such a thriving trade in second-hand slates. When laying slates on a roof, the largest were laid along the eaves at the bottom of the roof where there was greatest structural support. The slates were graded in size up to the ridge tiles where the smallest occur.

An example of Oak box frame design with Horsham slate roof at Itchingfield

Pitched Horsham Stones were revealed in excavations on an early medieval house site under what is now the Roffey bypass running past Leechpool Woods. Some of the stone had been used for a fireplace in the centre of the hall. When stones are pitched they are laid thin edge tilted into the ground at a slight angle. The footings were made of Hastings Sandstone with Horsham Stone on top. The Horsham Stone could have been dug from Hurst Hill, Rusper. Early medieval farmhouses had compacted earth floors and over time the stone floors became part of the fabric of the buildings.

Dated 1615, 'Flagstones' stands opposite St Mary's Church in the Causeway in Horsham

On the right is a picture of a Horsham Stone porch roof at Edburton Church. Ripple marks can be seen on a roof tile in the bottom row.

Archaeological excavations of a medieval saltern mound near Bramber on the River Adur revealed a number of Horsham slates that clearly were used for roofing. It would appear that the building was used from the fourteenth to the nineteenth century. There are many such sites scattered all along the banks of the River Adur down to Shoreham. The salt industry was a major economic activity and an essential part of medieval society. Shallow salt pans and evaporating pits show how the salt was extracted from tidal water in the river. Much of this process was carried out under a timber and stone roof.

A low ridge running from Monks Gate to Nuthurst defines the scarp edge of Horsham Stone which dips gradually to the south. This ridge is a distinctive landform that is so characteristic of Horsham Stone. The ridge turns west towards Sedgewick Lane and continues to Denne Hill. Beyond the ridge a gentle slope leads away to Copsale and Southwater. All along the crest of the ridge a series of shallow pits can still be seen. All are overgrown, and many are infilled. Signs of workings are just visible on the surface as shallow depressions and in some cases, small ponds. The area around Sedgewick was productive and it appears that these pits date back to early medieval times. 'The Victoria County History of Sussex' refers to second-hand roofing tiles being sold in the Sedgewick area in the fourteenth century. Today, Sedgewick Park House has a spectacular display of Horsham Stone roofing, walling and pathways. It is quite likely that much of this stone has been recycled from earlier buildings in the area such as the Norman Keep that was close by, or was found when digging the moat that surrounded the castle.

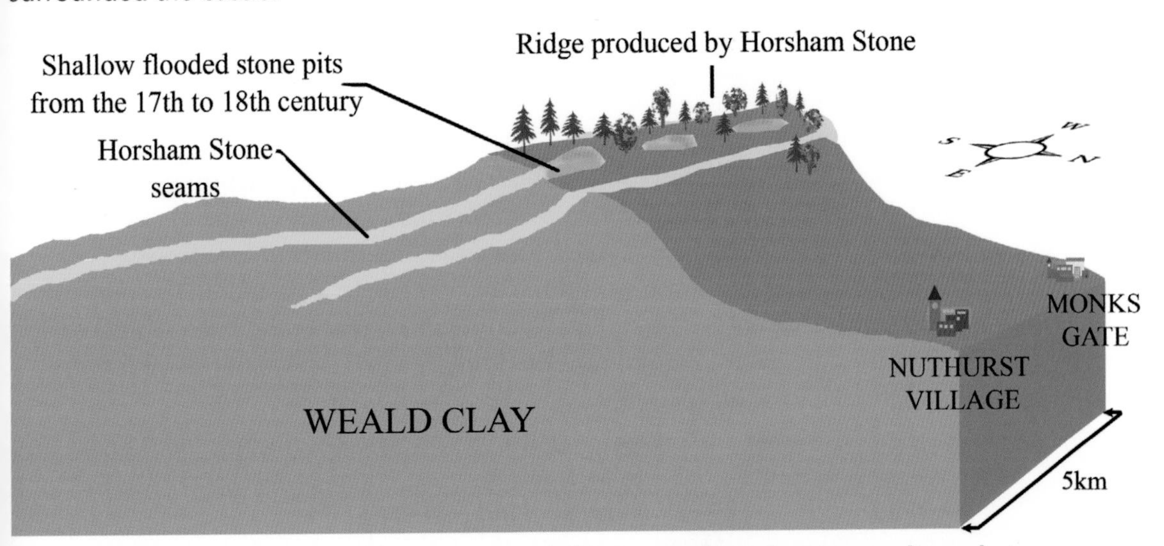

Sedgewick Park stone pits possibly started early in medieval times and last worked in mid-19th century

The southern edge of the main Horsham Stone outcrop runs from Sedgewick to Knepp Castle. Records show that slates were quarried from Knepp Manor in the late fifteenth century.

'The Victoria County History of Sussex' records that in the fourteenth century there was a well-established quarrying industry in the Horsham area. 'Horsham Stone roofing' was a term that appears in many historical references for this time. There were stone pits at Shortsfield Manor and possibly on Chesworth Manor in the fifteenth century. A 'stoneheler' was recorded in the Horsham Parish in 1450. A 'stone digger' was mentioned in 1574 in Southwater, along with other 'stonehelers' in the area.

The right to dig for stone on Chesworth Manor was leased by the Crown in 1583. Stone was being dug at Marlpost in 1592. In 1650 three stone pits are recorded in the Marlpost area, near Southwater. Stone continued to be dug extensively all around Horsham until the nineteenth century, often illegally. The famous Stammerham quarry is mentioned in records throughout the medieval period and was still being worked in 1896. Southwater Church was built in 1850 using stone from workings near Great House Farm, in Southwater and at Stammerham. By 1911 there was a limited demand for the Horsham Stone and many of the stone pits had closed down around the turn of the century. A stone pit at Tower Hill, Horsham existed between 1830 and 1868 but was closed by 1876.

Early 19th century paintings showing how stone was quarried and cut

The importance of the stone as a commercial product with a high value must have been realised very quickly and this would have led to the trading and transportation of the stone out of the area and across the county. Horsham Stone occurs in a wide range of Tudor buildings over much of West Sussex, and can be found also into parts of East Sussex and South Surrey. The high value of the stone would have given rise to a profitable trade in recycling stone and slabs from earlier buildings. Records show that in the late eighteenth century Horsham Stone slabs were dug up from the Roman road, Stane Street and used in houses in the Itchingfield and Slinfold area.

Many twelfth to seventeenth century farmhouses and manor houses show examples of Horsham Stone floors and porch steps. Churches such as Shipley, Billingshurst and Itchingfield have pathways made of Horsham Stone. Dating precisely when the slabs were laid down is difficult at times, as improvements and repairs were constant. The slabs were relatively easy to chisel into regular sizes to create a perfect fit with no gaps. A porch floor would have had a thicker slab projecting beyond the porch roof. The ripple-marked surfaces would have had particular appeal as anti-slip surfaces for steps and pathways.

Horsham Stone, ripple-marked slabs at Shipley Church

The north wall of Itchingfield Church has an unusual arrangement of Horsham Stone tiles as they have been set vertically, or tilted in the wall. One possible explanation could be that the best material arrived first and was used for corners and buttresses and the smaller pieces and irregular shapes were used as infill.

Details of the trading of Horsham Stone have been recorded as early as 1301 .... when 2,500 "scletes" or slates were bought for a barn in Thorney Manor, near Chichester. A hundred years later when repairs were being carried out at Warminghurst Church "some 9,000 blocks of Horsham Stone were obtained from Sedgewick". A lease in the Manor of Littlehampton made in 1468 stipulates that the "lessee John Cooke, should receive Horsham Stones for repairs from the lands of the abbess". Around this time there was a stonemason or `stonehelyer' of Horsham called Thomas Burgess, who had an apprentice called Jack Cade.

Hangleton, just to the north of Shoreham, is the site of a deserted medieval village. This village has been excavated a number of times and shows extensive use of Horsham Stone as roofing material and in floor slabs of simple dwellings. Horsham Stone roof tiles of varying sizes have been found; all have nail or peg holes. This village seems to have been abandoned sometime in the late medieval period. The majority of the stone would have been removed for use elsewhere, but clearly some stone remained within the fabric of buildings as they slowly fell down over time.

Records on the Wiston estate, near Steyning, record that in 1357 6p was paid for moss that was placed between Horsham roof tiles when the south chamber and gate were `healed'.

In 1550 the church at South Malling was pulled down and the Horsham Stone sold for 5 shillings and 8 pence.

Dr Burton was a local traveller who in 1751 recalls in his notes "from the quarries of stone they work out split slabs and use them instead of tiles to roof their houses......its warm tones lend a great beauty to many Sussex villages..........owing no doubt to the great weight of the roofing slabs and cost it does make on transport, now makes it expensive and would be disastrous to the unsubstantial timber of houses now built.

Sir Charles Lyell was a famous early geologist and scientist and in 1868 he visited Stammerham quarry near Christ's Hospital. He measured a detailed section of a quarry face and referred to the different types of stones that were being quarried....'as road material, rough paving, scrubstone and a compact rippled slab for indoor floors, steps and parlour'. Lyell set out some of the key principles on which the science of geology is based. The illustration on the next page gives a clear indication of how the beds were being used and the shallow depth to which the quarrymen dug to extract the stone.

Character of Strata	Provincial name	Thickness ft.	Thickness in.
1. Vegetable mould		1	6
2. Clay and Loam		9	6
3. Compact sandstone with deep undulating furrows on the upper surface	Rough causeway		4
4. Compact sandstone more indurated than the preceding road material	Scrubstone		4
5. Ditto	~		1
6. Ferruginous sandstone, which is pulverised for the manufacture of bricks	~	1	0
7. Blue soapy marl	~	1	0
8. Ferruginous sandstone like No 6	~	1	6
9. Hard calcareous sandstone, used for roads and rough paving	Ground pinning Sandstone	1	0
10. Compact sandstone of finer texture than any of the preceding; taken out in large slabs, and forming excellent paving stone for kitchens, etc, slightly marked with undulating furrows on its upper surface		2	0
11. Marl sunk but not worked	~	4	0
12. Stone reached by boring - depth unknown	~	0	0
		22	3

Lyell's measured section from Stammerham Quarry 1868

The expense of constructing houses with Horsham Stone and the development of the railways meant that cheaper stone could be brought to Sussex from all over Britain. Slates from North Wales became a common roofing material in the mid-nineteenth century and the use of Horsham Stone as a roofing material gradually declined. A survey of nineteenth century houses in Horsham shows this gradual transition from stone to slate roofing. Clay tiles and slate made construction easier. There was no longer a need for the massive, heavy timber-framed roofs to support Horsham Stone. True slate is a metamorphic rock which was once mudstone, clay or siltstone. This rock was buried deep in the Earth's crust and heated and pressurised over millions of years. It makes a superb impermeable material that can be split into 5mm thin slates. Pavements and roads were built using tarmac and cobblestone made of granite.

During the medieval period all the pavements in Horsham and villages across North-West Sussex would have been made of thick paving slabs. Many of these slabs would have been reused from other locations, such was the demand and value of the stones. Sadly, over the last 150 years these stones have been dug up and replaced with a wide range of man-made materials. Today, the Carfax in Horsham has a pedestrian area that has been built using York Stone from Yorkshire. The road around the Carfax has cobblestones quarried from Portugal.

View looking down the Causeway in Horsham

The historic Causeway in Horsham has the best remaining examples of Horsham Stone use in an urban environment. Many paving slabs show a wide range of geological features such as ripples, sole marks and trough cross-bedding. The majority of the buildings have Horsham Stone tiles of varying sizes. Pump Alley, off the Causeway has a good variety of Horsham Stone slabs. Horsham Museum has plenty of Horsham Stone on display in the garden at the rear of the building.

In St Mary's Church graveyard at the end of the Causeway, a number of tombs have large slabs of Horsham Stone showing excellent ripple marks. Many of the tombstones were reused as paving stones, a practice that was quite common in churches of the nineteenth century. The church roof at St Mary's is built of Horsham Stone slates. A number of houses along the Causeway have wells dating from before 1750. These have Horsham Stone lining the tops of the wells. Normandy, the area to the east of the church, still retains its Horsham Stone paving.

St Mary's Church in Horsham

Horsham Stone slab in St Mary's graveyard, Horsham

Here you can see the worn ripples of Horsham Stone

Under the pavements in the Causeway in Horsham, Horsham Stone culverts and drainage channels have been exposed showing how the stone was used in the construction of these essential drainage features. These have been given a tentative date of the early eighteenth century. Horsham Museum has Horsham Stone culverts beneath the garden.

Exposed 18th century drainage culverts

Horsham Stone used as a gravestone. Many examples can be found in church graveyards in North Sussex.

Horsham Stone paving slabs once ran down the slopes from Tower Hill past the Boar's Head pub and into Horsham. The Worthing Road gradually rises up a steep hill as it leaves Horsham. This slope is created by a large outcrop of Horsham Stone just below the surface. Shallow stone pits can be seen all along the crest of Denne Hill running west towards the Horsham bypass.

Many of the hammer ponds around Horsham have sluice channels and pathways lined with Horsham Stone. The sizes of the slabs and their structural strength made them ideal for this kind of use.

Some country stiles were made from Horsham Stone slabs. The slabs were usually set sideways into the ground along the base of the stile.

Until the opening of the new Horsham Stone quarry in 2004, the last working quarry was at Nowhurst, Strood Green between Broadbridge Heath and Clemsfold. This quarry closed in 1948. Both these quarries are very close to each other and occupy land just above the River Arun floodplain.

8 THE HISTORY OF THE USE OF SUSSEX MARBLE

The story of Sussex Marble is similar to that of Horsham Stone in that it can be traced back almost 2,000 years to Roman times. During this time the rock has acquired many names; 'Sussex Winklestone', the Large and the Small 'Paludina' Limestone, Petworth Marble, Charlwood Marble, Laughton Marble and Bethersden Marble. Geologists now use the term Viviparus Limestone. There are two types of limestone. The Large 'Paludina' Limestone was used mainly as an ornamental stone, had the larger shells, produced a more attractive polished finish and it occurs also in more continuous and thicker beds. The Small 'Paludina' had fossil shells about half the size of the Large 'Paludina' and is less frequently used as a polished marble. Both limestones outcrop across the Weald of Kent and East and West Sussex and this meant that they were freely available for decorative use in churches, substantial houses and civic buildings.

Purbeck Marble and Sussex Marble shafts at Boxgrove Priory

The use of the Purbeck Limestone is common throughout the Weald and this building stone is confused very often with Sussex Marble. Some very early examples of the use of Purbeck Limestone can be seen at Pulborough Church where there is a font dating to the twelfth century. Purbeck Limestone is geologically slightly older, around 140 million years and comes from the Upper Jurassic strata in Dorset, around the Isle of Purbeck. Today, there are still numerous quarries in the Swanage area extracting and carving monumental pieces. Purbeck Marble is composed typically of a mixture of bivalves and gastropods. It occurs in a range of colours; greens and blue/grey are particularly common. Chichester Cathedral has good examples of Purbeck Marble, found on tombstones and especially the superb piers and supporting shafts in the retrochoir. Sussex Marble can be seen in the large floor slabs laid down in the nave, and around the cloisters. By the west door thin moulding pieces have been used as a decorative feature, running just above ground level. These are now weathered but still recognisable. Several new polished Purbeck Marble shafts decorate the wall on either side of the west door.

The use of Sussex Marble was dictated by its geological composition. All limestones are subject to chemical weathering. The calcium shells and cement make them vulnerable to prolonged exposure to weak atmospheric acids. Sussex Marble is easily weathered by acidic rain. The acids break down the cement resulting in the fossils' shells falling out of the matrix. As a result of this weakness, Sussex Marble had a limited use externally, though it can be see in rough-cut form as paving stones, steps and infill in walls. Where it has been used outside, the stone is pockmarked, pitted and polished by generations of feet. When inside, the polish stone takes on a new attractive appearance and has been valued for hundreds of years.

When visiting churches, the visitor must be impressed by the workmanship shown in the tombstones and fonts. Hundreds of years ago the technology would have been rudimentary, yet an exceptional quality and finish was achieved and one has to admire the skills and dedication that workmen had in the past. Cutting the stone would have involved using a primitive type of saw. Limestone is relatively soft compared with other types of sedimentary rock. Minerals are measured on a hardness scale of 1 to 10, called Moh's scale. The mineral talc has a hardness of 1 and diamond 10. Calcite is the main mineral in Sussex Marble and has a hardness of 3. Quartz sand grains have a hardness of 7 and could have been used as an abrasive to remove the rough surface. A mixture of animal fats, clay and beeswax could have provided a polish. Today, rocks are polished using special grinding powders and synthetic polishes and automated electrical polish machines achieve in minutes what must have taken hours of hard sweat and tears!

actual size

Excavations at the Roman villa at Bignor have revealed a large block of Sussex Marble which shows signs of smoothing and polishing. The precise use of this block is debatable.

At the Roman staging post at Alfoldean a block of stone assumed to be Sussex Marble was found in an excavation trench in 1923. Verification of this find has been difficult as the specimen cannot be located.

Many West Sussex late Saxon and early Norman churches have Sussex Marble floor slabs; for example Greatham Church, Stopham and Poling. Greatham Church has a large Sussex Marble tomb slab in the churchyard, although dating it is difficult as it is weathered and covered in lichens. At Stopham the whole of the nave and the chancel are floored with Sussex Marble.

In East Sussex, Lullington Church in the Ouse valley has three Sussex Marble tomb slabs that were revealed during excavations in the 1960's. These early medieval slabs were badly weathered but still showed a hollow chamfer around the edges.

17th century engraved brasses set into Sussex Marble floor slabs at Stopham Church

The mining of Sussex Marble involved digging shallow pits or following beds of rock horizontally where they outcrop in valley or stream bottoms. The early medieval workings are difficult to identify owing to vegetation re-growth and farmers back-filling the pits. Broken ground and fragments of the limestone in the soil can help to track down the location of these small quarries. Workings that were near streams are now shallow ponds or marsh areas. Field place names indicate workings; for example near Billingshurst, Stonepits Rough is still marked on OS maps. Charlwood in Surrey was a major area of production of the Small 'Paludina' during medieval times and up to the late nineteenth century. The 1840 Tithe Map shows the location of old workings by their field names eg Pit Field, Stone Field and Pit Croft. The Woodland Trust has set up Nature Reserves in Glovers Wood and Edolph's Wood at Charlwood. Both these woodland areas have extensive, deep, flooded pits, remnants of the Charlwood Marble industry. Charlwood Church has a long path leading across the graveyard that is mainly composed of weathered Sussex Marble. During the nineteenth century there were many Sussex Marble paving slabs used in the village or as causeways across fields. These slabs were called 'causeys' but sadly, virtually all of these have been removed as they had pitted surfaces and had been fractured by frost and wear and tear.

In a 'Geological Treatise' published by Topley in 1875 many Sussex farms were identified as still producing small amounts of marble, probably for local use. North Barn Farm at East Chillington, north of Falmer has an excellent and unique example of Sussex Marble being used in wall rubble in a barn.

The Small 'Paludina' was worked mainly in the northern part of the Weald and eastwards towards Kent. Workings in Kent can be dated back to the early medieval period. Canterbury Cathedral has examples of its use as decorative shafts and floor slabs. A great number of Elizabethan and Jacobean houses have ornaments and fireplace surrounds carved out of Bethersden Marble.

View of the Northchapel mine pits today. Steep banks in this field show the site of shallow mine pits dug near Northchapel.

Some of the best documented accounts of the use and history of Sussex Marble come from the Petworth area. Sussex Marble production was perhaps the largest in West Sussex, especially in the eighteenth and nineteenth centuries. A large working area existed north of Petworth, near the village of Northchapel, at Mitchell Park, where limestone was quarried for nearly 200 years off and on. The main period of production at Mitchell Park was in the seventeenth century. The dates on Sussex Marble fonts in churches in the area indicate the demand and scale of workings; for example Kirdford 1620, Lurgashall 1661 and Northchapel 1662. The production area ran from the Surrey border, near Hascombe and Dunsfold and then, southwards towards Plaistow, Petworth and Kirdford and then east towards Wisborough Green and Billingshurst. This represents an area of over 30sq km. The marble beds lay at a depth of between 0.5m to 7m and the thickness varied from 3cm to 50cm. A number of marb beds occurred, separated by clay, silt or crumbly low quality marble.

The main period of working was in the seventeenth century and stream-side quarries supplied marble for the Petworth area, especially in the building of Petworth House. Some pits were over 5m deep and have left undulating, hummocky ground from the waste spoil. In the eighteenth and early nineteenth centuries many pavements in Petworth were rough-cut Sussex Marble. Mitchell Park is mentioned in a number of accounts about the history of Petworth Park.

Henry Percy, 9th Earl of Northumberland inherited the Petworth estate from his father. In 1606 Henry Percy was arrested on charges of conspiracy in the Gunpowder Plot and imprisoned in the Tower of London for fifteen years. Whilst in the Tower he spent much time designing new improvements to Petworth House. In 1615 he wrote 'The Computation of the New House at Petworth'. This consisted of grandiose, lavish extensions and improvements to Petworth House. The Earl clearly knew of the value and decorative properties of Sussex Marble which lay under his estate.

The following extract from his book illustrates the massive schemes he dreamt of whilst locked up in the Tower...

> *"the need to provide marble of the highest quality for 54 chimneys and fireplace surrounds... ....the amount to exceed 2,376 feet at 3 shillings per foot....marble to be polished and glassed.....for carrying the same load being 132 loads at 5 shillings per load"*

These elaborate plans took on even greater ambition with the plan to pave a main courtyard with over 40,000 square feet. In addition to this there was a need for 10,000 square feet of paving of curved steps. All this marble was to come from the northern part of the estate around Mitchell Park. On his release from the Tower the Earl spent the rest of his life 'on house arrest in Petworth'. The grand designs were never carried out although Petworth House does have a spectacular Marble Room in which the skirting board is made entirely of Sussex Marble. It has elegant moulding and stands 20cm high off the floor. The craftsmen skilfully fitted sections together around door frames and fireplaces. Numerous side tables which have thick, polished and shaped Sussex Marble tops can be seen throughout the house.

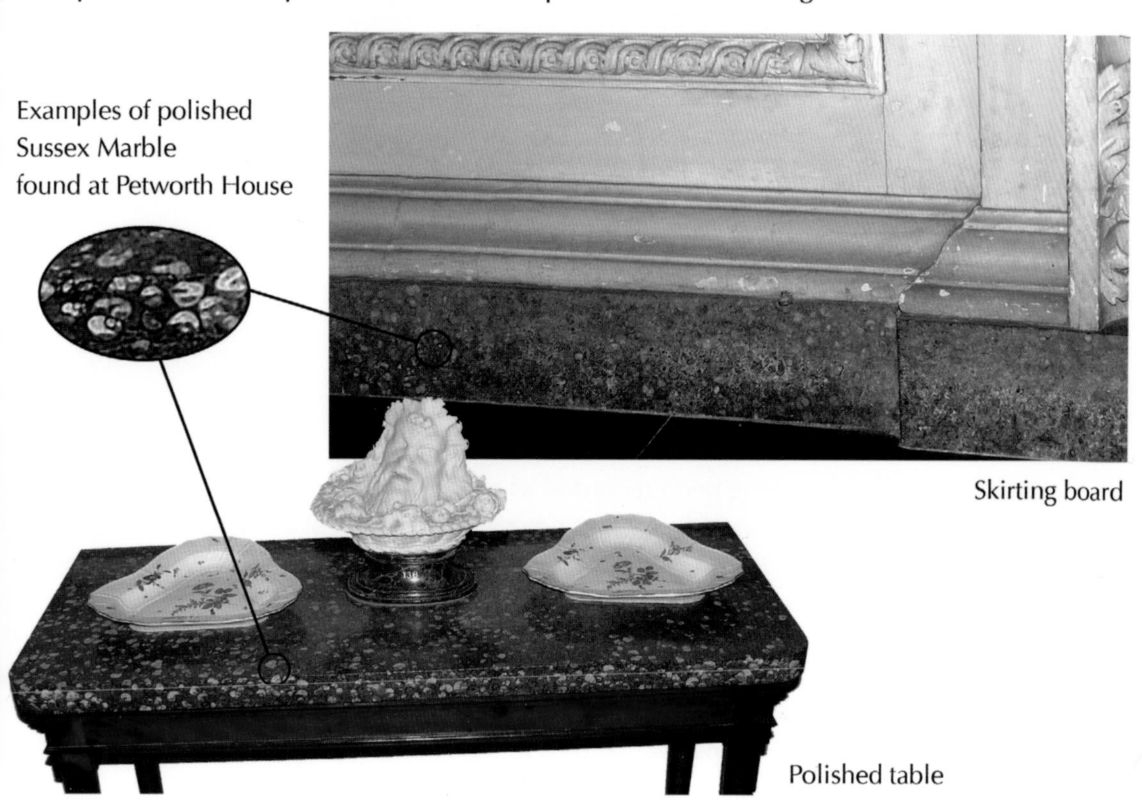

Examples of polished Sussex Marble found at Petworth House

Skirting board

Polished table

The Rev Arnold writing in 1864 in his 'History and Antiquities of Petworth' wrote......

"from the size of most of the shells of which it is formed it is more liable to decomposition than Purbeck marble; but it exceeds it in beauty, from their being so plainly apparent when viewed in a polished surface.....it was much sought after as sepulchral slabs, in which brasses are inserted.....it is so abundant in Petworth that one sees it used in the town even for ignoble purposes, such as for paving and for the construction of sinks and water-troughs... ...some of the thickest slabs are extracted from the parishes of Kirdford and Plaistow".

Petworth Church records show that in 1903 large Sussex Marble floor slabs were used in restoration work. These slabs came from Coolham and appear to indicate the last working of quarries in the area.

A rent roll of the Manor of Pallingham in 1639 shows that Nicholas West held copyhold of Lyeland and a meadow near Blackmell Wood which was licensed "to continue to quarry on the lands". This location is now thought to be near Crouchland Farm. One of these pits may have been worked by Richard Edwards in 1661.

The seam of marble from north of Petworth can be traced eastwards to Kirdford. Records show that in 1819 "marble of the highest perfection lay between 10 and 20 feet beneath the surface......embedded in flakes 9 to 12 inches thick".

The parish of Kirdford was a major productive area during the late medieval period. The old green road that runs north from Staples Hill to Plaistow passes many small pockmarked fields, especially near Crouchland Farm. Houses and farm tracks had rough-cut flagstones of Sussex Marble. The lych-gate at Kirdford Church is paved with several large slabs of Sussex Marble. Inside the church there is a Sussex Marble font dated 1620 and there are numerous Sussex Marble slabs in the nave. Slabs were valuable and it was common practice to lift and move good slabs around buildings or even sell them within the village.

Kirdford font

The village of Coolham has long been recorded as an important area for quarrying and a number of shallow pits dug alongside streams are recorded south of the village in the area near Hungerhill, Highfure, Slaughterbridge and Goringlee. Sussex Marble was still being produced in the Coolham area as late as 1903. It would appear that the last significant workings for Sussex Marble were in the Coolham area, near Sprouts Farm, around the turn of the last century. Some of the old green roads in this area still show their 'winklestone' foundation. A good example is Oldhouse Lane along which William Penn, the Quaker founder and first Governor of Pennsylvania used to travel from his house at Warminghurst to the Blue Idol Meeting House at Coolham.

Many farm buildings have Sussex Marble in their walls and the famous architect Sir Edward Lutyens incorporated Sussex Marble in several houses. Beds of Sussex Marble run west from Coolham towards Billingshurst. A number of quarries were sited near South House Farm and Stone Pits Rough.

It was in the early medieval period that the use of Sussex Marble became important. Some of the earliest church fonts made of Sussex Marble can be dated to the mid-twelfth century. Pulborough Church has a font of Purbeck Marble and Sussex Marble dated around this time. The design of the fonts has remained broadly the same for over 400 years. The typical Norman font had a square font top with the bowl recessed inside the block. A supporting central circular pedestal stood on a series of square steps. As additional features, four small circular shafts were placed between the font and the base, one at each corner of the latter. Designs followed a similar pattern throughout the medieval period. Sometimes the bowl section had shallow arcading cut around the perimeter. This design is still seen in fonts of the mid-seventeenth century. The proportions and thicknesses of fonts seem to vary with the availability of material and the stonemasons' ideas and inspiration. The limestone is cut smoothly with a better polish around the upper section, whilst the bases usually are rough-cut and do not show the fossils particularly well. Kirdford Church is unusual in that it has an octagonal bowl. Ifield Church near Crawley has a superb Sussex Marble font dated to 1180; only the basal step is a later addition. Unusually, it has the tops of its supporting pillars arching out into leaf-like carvings. The bowl section is still in excellent condition and shows the detailed structures of the fossil snails and the crushed shell matrix.

Two views of the font at Ifield

A number of tombs have Large 'Paludina' Sussex Marble slabs. At Pulborough and Thakeham Churches there are rough-cut tomb slabs dating to the mid-fifteenth century. The tomb at Pulborough originally had four small brass plates on each corner but now only one survives partially. Commemorative tablets were made of Purbeck and Sussex Marble in the early medieval period. By the sixteenth century Sussex Marble had replaced Purbeck Marble as the main decorative stone. Petworth and Northchapel Churches have examples of Sussex Marble that run from the sixteenth century to the nineteenth century. Pulborough, Up Marden and Billingshurst Churches have seventeenth century Sussex Marble tombs.

Sussex Marble tomb slabs now used as floor flagstones at Poynings Church

One of the most spectacular examples of craftsmanship using Sussex Marble can be seen in the Fitzalan Chapel at Arundel. The chantry chapel is dated to 1488 and is dedicated to William Fitzalan.

In his book Rev Arnold writes of a quarry opening up at Slaughter Farm in 1825.

The village of Trotton lies to the west of Midhurst where the church has a huge Sussex Marble sepulchral tombstone measuring 3m by 1.6m.

Tillingham Church has 12 Sussex Marble slabs laid around the chancel. These slabs are over 1.6m x 1.2m and are badly worn and pitted. They have been moved probably a number of times during their history.

Stopham Church has the aisle of the nave and chancel entirely floored with Sussex Marble. Set into the floor slabs is a unique feature, numerous brasses dating to the fifteenth century.

A number of country houses have sideboards, columns and fireplaces made of Sussex Marble. Several great houses like Knole and Godinton in Kent show intricate carvings and mouldings on fireplace surrounds. Parham House in West Sussex has window sills made of Sussex Marble. A good example of a rather plain Sussex Marble fireplace, dated around 1780, can be seen in Horsham Museum.

In 1700, during Wren's restoration of Westminster Abbey, Samuel Clothier and David Legge were asked to paint upon stone in the imitation of Sussex Marble.

Boxgrove Church has several pillars of Sussex Marble near the altar.

The church at West Lavington has massive corbels on the chancel arch. At Slaugham the elaborate lych-gate has Sussex Marble corbels.

Early medieval fonts had covers on the top of the bowl, fixed with locks to stop superstitious people stealing the holy water. The Archbishop of Canterbury ordered all fonts to be locked in 1236. The picture on the right shows detail of a late Norman font at Slaugham Church. The rough outline of a fish was an early Christian symbol, as the letters for the Greek word 'fish' are the intials of the primative creed, Jesus Christ.

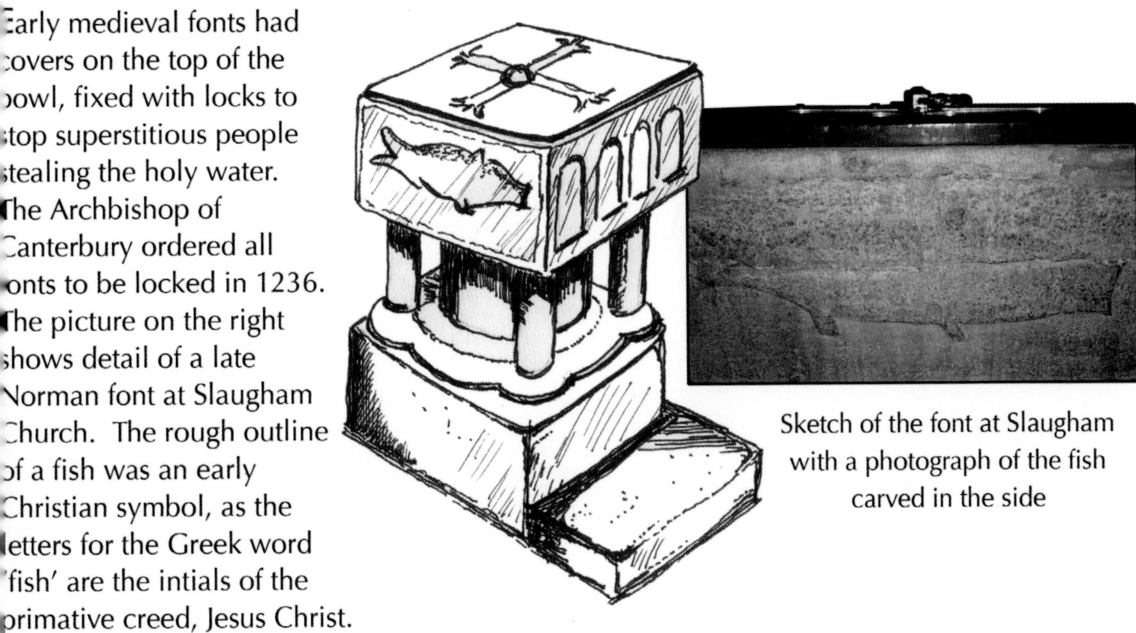

Sketch of the font at Slaugham with a photograph of the fish carved in the side

The history of each font is unique. Fonts have a central role in Christanity and as such, people placed great symbolic value in having a special piece of sculpture that was attractive and distinct. Many fonts were destroyed or simply turned into other ornaments for houses during the Civil War. The Puritans saw them as symbols of 'excess'. A significant number of church fonts can be dated to around the Restoration - the 1660's. At Lurgashall Church, a medieval font was destroyed and a second font was first used in 1662 when Charles II re-introduced the Prayer Book. The remains of the earlier font are still in the church. The style of the font at Lurgashall is repeated in other churches in the area where replacements at Dunsfold, Northchapel and Hascombe can be seen.

The font and date plate at Lurgashall Church. The square block faces cut into each piece of Sussex Marble represent a new design typical of the late 17th century.

Norman tub font and base carved in Large 'Paludina' Limestone Rudgwick Church

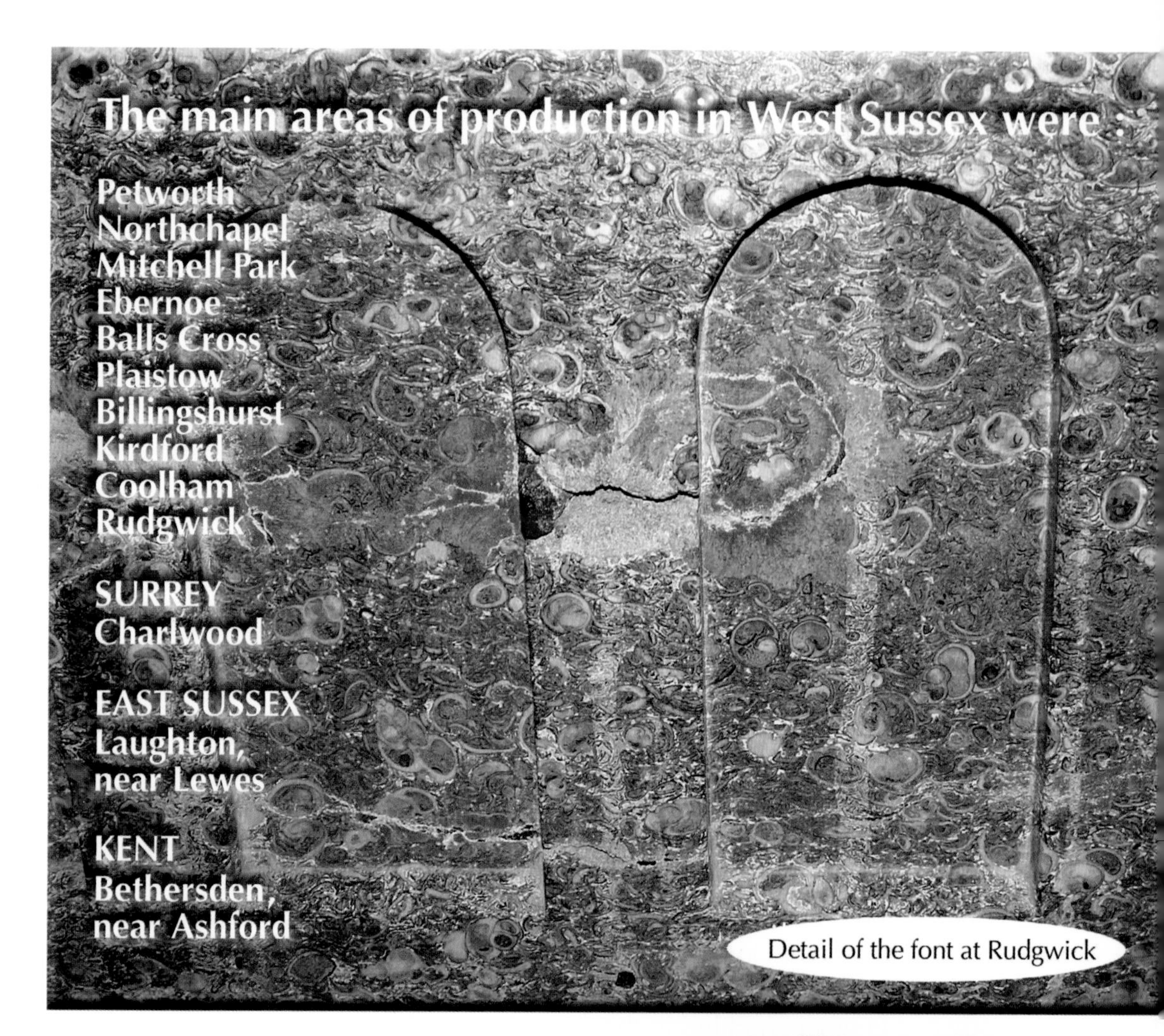

Detail of the font at Rudgwick

Throughout the medieval period churches became the main place where Sussex Marble was used. Billingshurst, Shipley and Thakeham Churches have numerous Sussex Marble paving slabs around the outside of them. Thakeham particularly is interesting in that it has several Sussex Marble steps leading up to the church. During this time the extending and repairing of churches inevitably meant that slabs were reused for different purposes. Poling Church, near Arundel has a late Saxon altar cut from a massive piece of Sussex Marble. Tombstones of Sussex Marble have been re-laid as flooring around the altar. Poling has a very rare example of a memorial brass set into Sussex Marble. It is dedicated to Walter Davy, vicar at Poling from 1442 until 1499.

Mortar bowl carved in Large 'Paludina' Limestone, Horsham Museum

9 HORSHAM STONE TODAY

Horsham Stone has not been quarried since the 1930's when a small quarry operated at Nowhurst, near Broadbridge Heath. The Historic Horsham Stone Company reopened old delve fields in 2004 and are extracting stone once again.

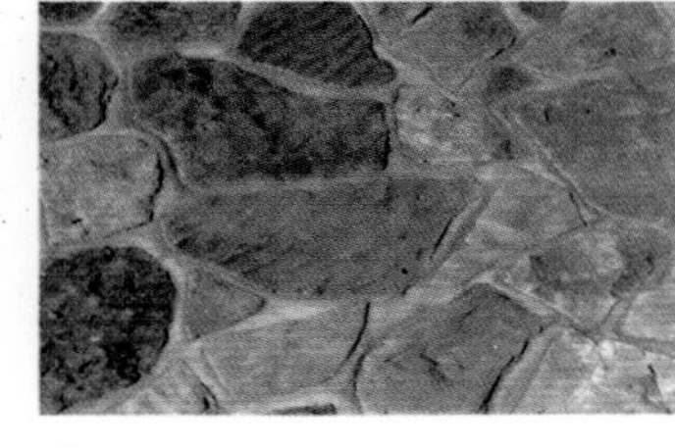

Flag Stones
These are available as shapes produced randomly by nature or sawn and hand dressed with square edges. Enormous flags up to 2.5m long can be produced!

This bird table has been constructed using Horsham Stone.

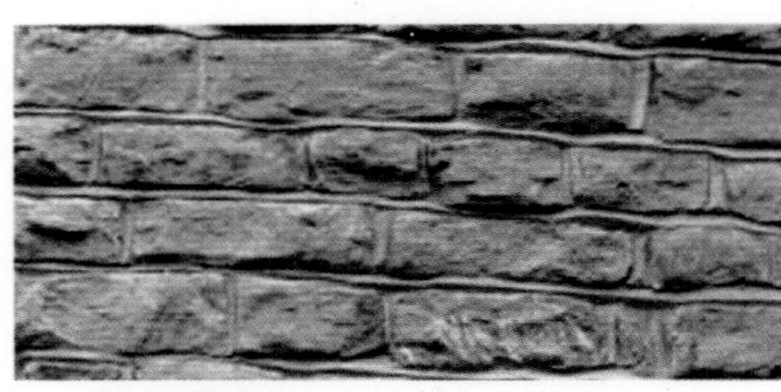

Walling Stone
This comes in a variety of subtle colours allowing for the matching of new stone with existing construction. It is available in natural, cropped or dressed face. It can be cut to any size required.

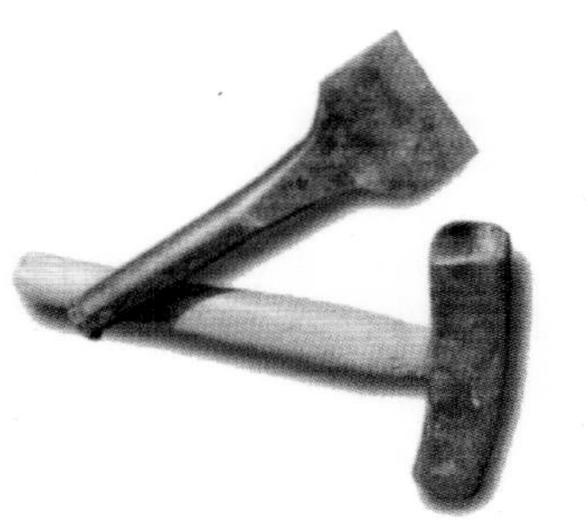

Rockery and Feature Stones
A vast range of rockery and feature stones is available, featuring many of the elements that make Horsham Stone so versatile and adaptable. Combinations of features and stone can be used to dramatic and creative effect.

Roofing Slates

Horsham Stone is most famously used for roofing slates. The slate is produced in the traditional way, by hand, splitting the slates along the stone's natural cleavage. The slates are then sawn and dressed by hand, by stonemasons to produce 'old look' slates. These can be cut to any size.

Historic Horsham Stone

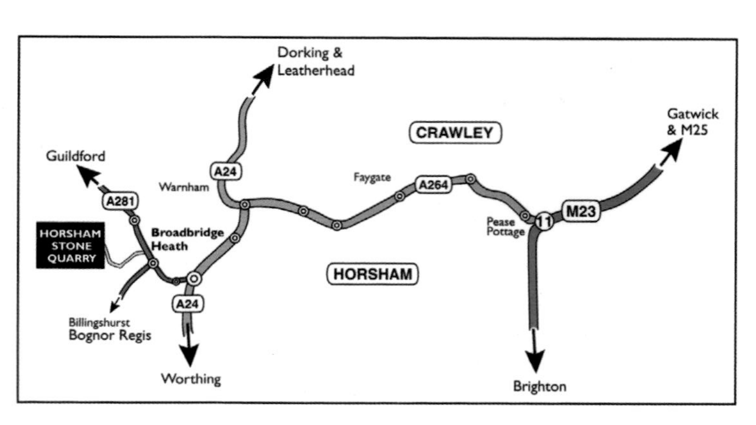

If you are interested in purchasing Horsham Stone products
You can contact
Simon Stainer at
Historic Horsham Stone
Lower Broadbridge Farm
Broadbridge Heath
West Sussex
RH12 3LR
Telephone: 01403 276550
Fax: 01403 276551
Email: info@horshamstone.co.uk

SOME PLACES TO VISIT TO SEE SUSSEX MARBLE

Billingshurst Church
Bosham Church
Boxgrove Priory
Chichester Cathedral – *floor slabs, tombs, shafts and capitals. In the twelfth century Bishop Seffrid II expressed a desire to use more Sussex Marble alongside Purbeck Marble.*
East Preston Church
Ferring Church
Greatham Church
Ifield Church
Lurgashall Church
New Shoreham Church
Northchapel Church
Parham House
Petworth House
Pulborough Church
Rudgwick Church
Thakeham Church
Trotton Church
Shipley Church
Stopham Church
Warminghurst Church
West Wittering Church
Winchelsea Church
Yapton Church

SOME PLACES TO SEE HORSHAM STONE

Places mentioned have excellent examples of timber-framed houses that show Horsham Stone roofing.

Ardingly and Church
Bignor
Bury and Church
Charlwood and Church
Clayton
Cowfold
Cuckfield and Church
Findon
Horsham – *Causeway houses and pavements, Horsham Museum garden, buildings around the Carfax, Park House*
Itchingfield and Church
Lewes
Nuthurst and Church
Pulborough and Church
Rudgwick and Church
Rusper and Church
Steyning, several streets near the Church
Slaugham
Stopham
Sutton
Thakeham and Church
Twineham
Upper Beeding

GLOSSARY

Anoxic	**An environment low in oxygen eg a swamp.**
Basin	**A large, low-lying area such as a delta or shallow sea, where sediment builds up over millions of years. Gradually, the weight of the sediment causes the basin to sink, thus allowing a great thickness of sediment to accumulate.**
Basin Cast	**A shallow depression eroded into sand by water currents can form a mould into which sand can be deposited later. This will produce a basin mould and a basin cast. Wealden basin casts can be over 5m across and 6cm thick.**
Beaconites	**A type of trace fossil. The animal that made these small, sinuous trails is debatable – one possibility is a small shrimp-like animal.**
Bedforms	**A structure on a bedding plane formed by water or wind eg a ripple mark.**
Bedding Plane	**Dividing plane or line between two layers of sedimentary rocks.**
Bivalves	**A group of molluscs that have two shells or valves. Typical species would be cockles, oysters and mussels.**
Bioturbation	**Where sediment has been disturbed by burrowing organisms or by plant growth.**
Brackish	**Water that is a mix of fresh and salt water, typical of an estuary.**
Braided Channel	**A river that has numerous channels and pebble islands.**
Calcite	**A mineral composed of calcium carbonate, which is a major mineral in limestone.**
Calcareous Sandstone	**A sandstone that has calcite around the sand grains acting as a cement.**
Carbonation	**A chemical process of weathering during which minerals containing calcium are transformed into carbonates.**

Cement	A term to describe any mineral that crystallises between particles of sediment to form a rock. Calcite, quartz and pyrite are the commonest types of cement.
Cleavage	The property of a rock to split along thin lines of weakness. This characteristic is typical of Horsham Stone and is used to create roofing 'slates'.
Cretaceous Period	A unit of geological time that lasted from 130 million years ago to 65 million years ago.
Cross-bedding	Layers or beds of sediment laid down at an inclined angle to horizontal beds. Formed due to changing current flow. Can be formed by tidal or wind-driven currents.
Cycles of Sedimentation	A phrase used to describe how a series of sediments is repeatedly deposited over time. Seasonal and climatic changes can produce this effect.
Desiccation Cracks	Sometimes called sun-cracks. These are structures that form in sediments that are exposed to high temperatures such as a tropical sun. The sediment dries out and shrinks to produce polygonal crack lines.
Fissile	The property of a rock that allows it to split into thin sheets or layers. This is a form of cleavage.
Flaggy Sandstone	A bed of sandstone that splits easily into thin slabs that can be used for flagstones.
Flood-plain	An area on either side of a river where mud, sand and silt (alluvium) are deposited when the river overflows during flooding.
Fluvial	A river environment.
Gastrolith	Highly polished stomach stones believed to have been used by dinosaurs to assist with digestion.
Gastropod	A group of molluscs with a single calcareous shell. Varieties include whelks, snails and limpets.
Lacustrine	A lake environment.

Ladder Ripples	**An unusual form of ripple that has two lines of ripples running at right angles to each other.**
Laminations	**Thin layers or beds of sediment usually 2-5mm thick. Silts and fine sand are deposited in slow-moving water as laminated sediments.**
Laurasia	**The name of the northern super continent that existed over 200 million years ago.**
Lepidotes	**A large freshwater fish that lived in rivers and lakes during the Lower Cretaceous Period.**
Limestone	**A sedimentary rock that is composed of calcareous material such as fossils or cement.**
Healing	**A medieval term to describe the repairing of a stone roof with new 'slates'.**
High Weald	**A geographical area running across Central Sussex and Kent that has a higher relief than the Weald Clay vales that surround it.**
Hybodus	**A freshwater shark that lived during the Cretaceous period.**
Jurassic Period	**A famous geological period that lasted from 206 million years ago to 144 million years ago.**
Marble	**Marble is produced when limestone is buried deep in the Earth's crus and altered by high temperatures. This is a metamorphic process.**
Matrix	**Background material in which a fossil is embedded.**
Palaeoenvironment	**The reconstruction of a landscape in the geological past.**
Paludina Limestone	**Another name for Sussex Marble. 'Paludina' is the nineteenth century fossil name for the snail shell found in the limestone.**
Purbeck Beds	**A series of sedimentary rocks that were laid down in the Upper Jurassic period, mainly found in East Dorset.**
Quartz	**A common rock forming mineral composed of silica and oxygen.**
Ripple Marks	**Bedforms produced by flowing water or wind. In the Wealden swamp ripples were formed by river and tidal currents.**

Sandstones	**A type of sedimentary rock that contains mineral grains of sand-sized particles. The sizes range from 2mm diameter to 0.002mm.**
Scarp	**A term used to describe a steep, or prominent slope formed by strata dipping into the ground.**
Scute	**Horn-like material that forms exoskeletal plates to protect the shells of turtles.**
Soil Horizon	**These are layers with different characteristics within a bed of soil. Horizons can be preserved when the soil material is cemented and turns into rock. This is called a palaeosoil.**
Sole Marks	**A type of bedform that is created when turbulent water forms small scoop marks in sand. These are typical of tidal rivers and where currents meet in a river channel.**
Sussex Marble	**A broad, generic name used since medieval times to describe a shelly limestone that polishes easily to give a marble effect. Also known as Petworth Marble, Laughton Marble, Charlwood Marble and Bethersden Marble. The term 'Paludina' Limestone has also been widely used since the early nineteenth century.**
Theropod	**A bipedal, carnivorous dinosaur.**
Trace Fossils	**Imprints left by organisms in sediment eg a dinosaur footprint or worm burrow.**
Transgression	**A marine incursion or advance of the sea over the land.**
Trough Cross-Bedding	**A form of cross-bedding produced when ripples and underwater sandbanks migrate with turbulent currents.**
Viviparus Limestone	**A modern palaeontological term for the 'Paludina' Limestone.**
Weald	**The Anglo-Saxons used the word Andredsweald to describe the central area of Sussex and Kent.**
Weald Clay	**A sequence of mainly clay with thinner beds of sandstones, siltstones and limestones that forms part of the Lower Cretaceous period.**

USEFUL ORGANISATIONS & LINKS

Booth Museum, 194 Dyke Road, Brighton.	01273 292771
Horsham Museum, 9 The Causeway, Horsham.	01403 254959
Steyning Museum, Church Street, Steyning.	01903 813333
Sussex Historic Churches Trust.	www.sussexhistoricchurches.org.uk
Worthing Museum, Chapel Road, Worthing.	01903 239999

LOCAL GEOLOGICAL GROUPS

Brighton and Hove Geological Society.	Contact John Cooper 01273 292780
Horsham Geological Field Club.	Contact Gill Woodhatch 01403 250371
Sussex Mineral and Lapidary Society.	Contact John Pearce 01444 233958
The Geological Association.	Contact Sarah Stafford 0207 434 9298
West Sussex Geological Society.	Contact Pat Waterson 01903 265715

FURTHER READING AND REFERENCES

Allen P. (1958) Geology of the Central Weald and the Hastings Beds, Geologists Association No 24. London.

Arnold Rev. F.H. (1864) History and Antiquities of Petworth.

Brooks Ken (2001) Geology and Fossils of the Hastings Area. Pub by K. Brooks.

British Geological Survey No 319, (1987) Geology of the country around Lewes. HMSO. London.

British Geological Survey No 302, (1993) Geology of the country around Horsham. HMSO. London.

British Geology Survey No 318/333 (1988) Geology of the country around Brighton and Worthing. HMSO. London.

Edmunds F.H. (1954) The Wealden District 3rd Edition, British Regional Series, Dept of Scientific and Industrial Research, Geological Survey and Museum. HMSO. London.

Gibbons W. (1981) The Weald. Unwin. London.

Lord Leconfield (1954) Petworth Manor in the Eighteenth Century. OUP.

London Natural History Museum (2001), British Mesozoic Fossils, 6th Edition. London.

Lucas, E.V. (1935) Highways and Byways in Sussex. Macmillan. London.

Kenyon P.E. (1961) Petworth Town and Trades 1610 to 1760. SAC Vol 99

Mantell G. (1827) Illustrations of the Geology of Sussex. London.

Nairn I. & Pevsner N. (2001) The Buildings of England: Sussex. Penguin Books.

Ruffell A, Ross A, and Taylor K. (1996) Geologists Association Guide No 55, Early Cretaceous Environments of the Weald. London.

Sussex Notes and Queries: Full collection of back issues held at Horsham Museum.

The Victoria History of the Counties of England. (1907): Sussex. Archibald Constable & Company Ltd. London

PICTURE CREDITS

PETER AUSTEN
ROGER BIRCH
KEN BROOKS
PETER GREEN
DR E JARZENBOWSKI
IAN MCALISTER
JOHN SIBBICK
GEOFF TOYNES
PETER WEBSTER
BIGNOR ROMAN VILLA
HORSHAM HISTORICAL SOCIETY
HORSHAM MUSEUM
SUSSEX ARCHAEOLOGICAL COLLECTIONS
PETWORTH HOUSE: NATIONAL TRUST

ACKNOWLEDGEMENTS

The author has benefited from the expertise, advice and encouragement from many people during the preparation of this book. In particular, I would like to thank Peter Webster, Peter Green, Frank Diggon, Ellis Owen, Sylvia Standing, Dr John Radley, Ken Brooks, Diana Page, Adrian Stevens, Ian McAlister, Jeremy Knight and Simon Stainer of the Historic Horsham Stone Company.

CHURCHES

BOXGROVE PRIORY
ST MARY'S HORSHAM
IFIELD
POLING
RUDGWICK
SHIPLEY
EDBURTON
STOPHAM
KIRDFORD
POYNINGS
SLAUGHAM
WARMINGHURST

SPONSORS

Financial support for this book has been kindly provided by the following....

Historic Horsham Stone

DORNWORTH FINANCIAL CONSULTANTS
111, HIGH STREET, CRANLEIGH, SURREY

learning
and skills
beacon
awarded by
the department for
education and skills

Set into the flint wall on the side of East Dean Church in the upper Lavant valley is this slab of Sussex Marble. It has weathered with a red tint and bears the following inscription.